THE INDIAN RUBBER ECONOMY
History, Analysis and Policy Perspectives

THE INDIAN RUBBER ECONOMY
History, Analysis and Policy Perspectives

R.G. Unny
V. Haridasan
Rubber Board
Government of India
Kottayam, Kerala
India

Kees Burger
Hidde P. Smit
Wouter Zant
Economic and Social Institute
Free University, Amsterdam
the Netherlands

MANOHAR
1995

ISBN 81-7304-131-8

First Published 1995

© IDPAD, 1995

Published by
Ajay Kumar Jain
Manohar Publishers & Distributors
2/6 Ansari Road, Daryaganj
New Delhi - 110002

Lasertypeset by
AJ Software Publishing Co. Pvt. Ltd.
305, Durga Chambers, 1333, D.B. Gupta Road
Karol Bagh, New Delhi - 110005

Printed at
Rajkamal Electric Press
G.T. Karnal Road
Delhi - 110033

CONTENTS

FOREWORD

The project **Policy formulation and perspectives for the Indian natural rubber industry in a changing national and international context** is financed from Phase 3 of the Indo-Dutch Programme on Alternatives in Development (IDPAD). The project is undertaken jointly by the Rubber Board of India and the Economic and Social Institute (ESI), Free University, Amsterdam. The project work started in January 1991 and was scheduled to be finalised at the end of 1992.

The objectives of the project are to quantify the perspectives of the Indian natural rubber production and processing industry in a rapidly changing international context, to forecast likely developments in this industry and to assess and formulate national policies in order to optimally cope with international changes. At the time of submitting the original project proposal, March 1989, the extent and impact of the changes in the Indian economic policy, as became clear in the early 1990s could not be envisaged. A request was made for an extension of the project. The extension was approved by IDPAD. The final draft of the report on which this book is based was submitted in January 1994. A revision, based on a referee report was submitted in July 1994. In both cases the analysis was based on data up to 1992 at the latest. Figures for 1993 and later are projections.

A particular aspect was to provide for user-friendly software in order to update the current analyses as a basis for future planning and policy making. The complete database and computer simulation software are available at the Rubber Board and at the Economic and Social Institute.

The interpretation, findings and conclusions, expressed in the documents are entirely those of the authors and do not necessarily reflect the views of the Rubber Board, the Governments concerned, or other connected organisations. It is hoped that this document will provide an opportunity to those interested in the subject to enhance their awareness of modelling analysis as a tool that can be used for policy formulation. Such an analysis is normally done at a macro level. For the purpose of policy implementation a mapping should therefore be sought from such formulations in statistical terms to the reality of extension work, taxes and subsidies and the like. The focus is on the methodology rather than on the numerical values of projections appearing in the book as these depend on the assumptions regarding future policies to be actually implemented.

The project directors like to express their gratitude to IDPAD, and to the Governments of India and the Netherlands respectively for their financial support. They also very much appreciate the cordial atmosphere in which all work has been done. In this respect, also on behalf of the authors of the report, they would like to thank all involved, including Mrs. E. Lalithakumari, Mr. G. Mohanachandran of the Rubber Board, and Mr. Robert-Paul Berben, Mrs. Mariska Blok, Mr. Arjan Heyma, Mr. Hans Hoogeveen and Mrs. Hanneke van Wouwe of the Economic and Social Institute.

Mrs. J. Lalithambika, I.A.S.   Dr. Hidde P. Smit
Project Director and   Project Director and
Chairman, Rubber Board   Division Chief Economic Research
Government of India   Economic and Social Institute
Kottayam, Kerala   Free University
India   Amsterdam
                                                               the Netherlands

PREFACE

The project

This report presents the findings resulting from the project entitled
"Policy formulation and perspectives for the Indian natural rubber
industry in a changing national and international context". The project
was carried out jointly by the Rubber Board, Government of India,
Kottayam, Kerala, India, and the Economic and Social Institute, Free
University, Amsterdam, the Netherlands. The project is part of phase 3
of the Indo-Dutch Programme on Alternatives in Development (IDPAD),
funded by the governments of India and the Netherlands. The project
was originally planned to be implemented during May 1989 - April
1991. However, for external reasons the study could start only in
January 1991.

A. *Background and objectives*

As mentioned in the original project proposal, written in late 1988, with
respect to production, trade and processing of natural rubber the
following aspects come to the fore:

- India has a natural rubber production and processing sector,
  which is not significantly open to international trade;
- the arrangement of regular imports of natural rubber is necessary
  as India is not fully self-sufficient in natural rubber; a small-
  scale buffer stock scheme for natural rubber has been in
  operation since 1986 to prevent high fluctuations in domestic
  rubber prices;
- consumption of natural and synthetic rubber are influenced by
  developments in the tyre industry, in particular by joint
  production with foreign firms;

- consumption may also be heavily influenced by possible changes in the bias, partly policy-based towards natural rubber's share in the domestic market, as compared with its share in the international market;
- the above facts require careful monitoring of production and consumption figures for rubber.

For the purpose of keeping an important sector of the Indian economy running smoothly, it would be very useful to develop a detailed methodology to better monitor and forecast developments in rubber production and consumption. In this connection the (future) viability of and the need for various policies on (re)planting, production, trade, subsidies, buffer stocks and pricing needs to be assessed. It would then be essential that this methodology is transferred and kept operational in the Indian Rubber Board and other policy formulating and/or implementing bodies.

B. Objectives

The objectives of the project are to quantify the prospects of natural rubber production and processing industry in India in a rapidly changing international context and to assess and formulate national policies in order to optimally cope with international changes.

C. Overview of the original project outline

The project consists of the following four partly overlapping parts:

i)   Collection of the available statistics regarding natural rubber and synthetic rubber production in India, the pattern of new planting and replanting so far undertaken, the present consumption pattern of natural rubber versus synthetic rubber, industry-wise consumption of rubber in India, pattern of import, etc. Evaluation of the prospects of expansion of natural rubber production in India with reference to area planting available, replanting of old uneconomic plantations with high yielding varieties, possibilities of increase in productivity and other relevant factors to project the pattern of natural rubber production up to 2010 AD. Alongside, the prospects of synthetic rubber production are also analyzed.

ii) Comprehensive review of natural rubber and synthetic rubber production is undertaken with reference to the demand in India from various large scale and small scale rubber consuming industries. An analysis is carried out to project the future trends in demand.

iii) This projected supply and demand pattern is inter-linked with the respective prices per tonne of synthetic rubber and natural rubber in India as well as the price trend of possible imports. Collating all these aspects of supply, demand and prices in the Indian as well as in the international context, an effort is made to formulate guidelines which can form the basis of the national policy on rubber to ensure optimum use of the available resources.

iv) Finally, a series of small training workshops to be organised for the staff of the Rubber Board to ensure the dissemination of this analytical tool for India for policy formulation and adjustment.

D. Extension of the original project

The enhanced relevance for present-day policy and the great interest shown in the study, its approach and the preliminary results, led to the suggestion to extend the project, which was designed in 1988 before the increase in the pace of economic liberalization.

First of all, more details were suggested for inclusion in the study. This refers to the new international trade policy, exports of vehicles, tyres and other rubber goods, the "import for export production of rubber goods" policy, the need for a harmonious lowering of import duties, excise duties and 'cess' and (more similar) details that were beyond the initial scope of the project.

Apart from workshops for personnel of the Rubber Board, similar workshops were suggested for representatives of rubber producing and consuming industries, their associations, as well as for the ministries.

Secondly, a good analysis and transfer of the data, the model and the computer software to parties involved in the production of rubber and rubber goods in India and not only to the Rubber Board, would allow regular monitoring and policy adjustment in the years to come.

Summary of the project

The philosophy of the project is as follows. Policy implementation in the Indian rubber economy occurs in many areas such as planning of planting, replanting subsidies, indirect taxes, import duties and pricing. In many cases it is necessary to assess the effect of proposed (changes in) measures. Such an assessment may e.g. take the form of; 'calculate what happens to e.g. national production, import and export and prices if we extend rubber area in a certain non-traditional area by so much'. This requires that relationships are established in quantitative terms between the policy variable (in this case rubber area in a non-traditional area) and the variables that matter: production, prices and therefore income etc. for farmers, government etc. The relationships normally take the form of a model, formulated in mathematical terms. Developing such a model is the main theme of this project and this report. Such a model is based on the past and adjusted so as to cover the future as well. This is the reason why a lot of detail is given in this report which has been used for establishing the model. This should enable the interested reader to better understand why the model has been designed and develop in the way reported here. Afterwards, of course, projections are made and a number of policy scenarios are assessed using the model. However, the number of combinations of policy scenarios is virtually unlimited. For that reason the objective of this project was also to establish the modelling framework at the Rubber Board for further running of selected policy scenarios and for further updating and improvement. It needs to be stressed that obviously, as an example, when this report mentions replanting of so much, that then the responsible authorities have to find ways to convince the farmers to get that amount replanting in the ground. This is a separate discipline which is not applied in this report.

The project work has originally been designed to include the four phases mentioned under c. Because of the late start, it was preferred to enter various phases simultaneously. First, the available statistics regarding natural rubber and synthetic rubber production in India, the pattern of new planting and replanting so far undertaken, the present consumption pattern of natural rubber versus synthetic rubber, industry-wise consumption of rubber in India, pattern of import, etc. are studied. The prospect of expansion of natural rubber production in India with reference to areas available, replanting of old uneconomic plantation with high yielding varieties, possibilities of increase in productivity and other relevant factors is examined with the aim to project the pattern of natural rubber production up to AD 2010. A sample survey is under-taken with reference to planting and production of natural rubber in the recently changed economic environment so as to provide a more sound basis for forecasting natural rubber supply potential in India. Simultaneously, the prospects of synthetic rubber production are also analyzed. A detailed analysis is carried out to project future demand for all rubber based on detailed models of demand for the various modes of transport and the tyres and rubber required for it, as well as non-tyre rubber demand. Then, this projected supply and demand pattern is inter-linked with the price per tonne of synthetic rubber and natural rubber in India as well as the price trend of possible imports. Collating all these aspects of supply, demand and prices in the Indian as well as in the international context provides the basis to formulate national policies for the rubber sector to ensure optimum use of available resources. Finally, an essential and time-consuming element of the project is the development of use-friendly software, the transfer of the software, the model and the databank of India and a series of training sessions in using and further updating and improving the computer simulation model. In this sense the project will be fruitful for many years to come.

A broad review of the structure of the report

Part I of this report gives a review of the three types of rubber supplied. This is done in Chapter 1 for natural rubber (NR), in Chapter 2 for synthetic rubber (SR) and in Chapter 3 for reclaimed rubber (RR). The main theme of this report is supply of and demand for natural rubber. For that reason the analysis of the supply side of natural rubber, in particular in terms of past planting and production behaviour and estimated production potential is described in detail in Part II, Chapters 4, 5 and 6. The demand side is discussed elaborately in Part III. This part starts with Chapter 7 which gives a general overview of the demand side and proceeds to develop the analytical approach. This is then followed by the empirical analysis for each category in Chapter 8 followed by analyses to split the total demand for rubber into NR, SR and RR. In this regard prices may often play a role. They in turn are influenced by the interaction between demand, supply and various types of stocks which is described in Part IV, Chapters 9 and 10. The outlook for the Indian rubber economy and policy simulations and suggestions are also presented and evaluated in Chapter 10. Conclusions and recommendations are given in the last part in Chapter 11.

The report contains quite a bit of econometrics. However, there is no need to go through and understand all technicalities in order to comprehend the approach and the results. If the reader so wishes, he can follow the easy route and concentrate on Chapters 1 to 4, glance through Chapters 5 to 6, concentrating on the verbal explanations and the graphs, read Chapter 7, glance through Chapter 8 in the same way as with Chapters 5 to 6, and finally read Chapters 10 and 11, thereby skipping the equations.

Part I
An Overview of Rubber Supply

1

THE NATURAL RUBBER INDUSTRY

1.1 Introduction

In this chapter a description is presented of historical developments in natural rubber production. The purpose of this chapter is to provide background information for the quantitative analysis of natural rubber supply in chapters 4, 5 and 6. Such a quantitative analysis draws heavily on developments in the past to indicate future patterns. For that reason a considerable amount of historical information was collected of which a part is reproduced in this report for the benefit of the reader who wishes to appreciate the approach described. The last section of this chapter reviews the past Five-Year Plan targets and performance in planting of natural rubber.

1.2 The introduction and development of the natural rubber sector until independence

India is mainly responsible for the introduction of natural rubber to the East. It was the India Office, London which financed Sir Henry Wickham's expedition to the Amazon valley in Brazil to procure rubber seeds in 1876. Wickham's collection of seeds from the Amazon valley was brought to the Kew Gardens, London, from where seedlings were sent to Ceylon (Sri Lanka), Malaya (West Malaysia) and India.

The period 1904-1910 saw considerable activity in *Hevea* rubber planting. During that period two important rubber companies i.e. Travancore Rubber and Produce Company and the Malayalam Rubber and Produce Company came into existence. A number of small plantations also came into being around that period. By 1910 Mundakayam had become the leading centre of rubber plantations in India with an area of about 4,000 ha. This was around half of the area under rubber plantation then. By that time Indians also began to take interest in planting rubber.

Rubber was first planted in the erstwhile Cochin State at Palapilly in 1905 (Trichur District, Kerala).

With the invention of the pneumatic tyre and the development of internal combustion engines by the close of the last century, a frantic attempt was made all over the world to obtain more rubber. The world production of rubber in 1900 was about 45,000 tonnes while the demand was 52,500 tonnes. This imbalance could not continue for long without an alternative source of supply. The increased demand naturally raised the price of rubber. By 1900 a marked increased in the price began to be seen. The all time record was reached in 1910. This exorbitant price led to a scramble for planting rubber in the West Coast of India. The same happened in many other countries.

The tide turned during the depression years and the International Rubber Regulation Agreement (IRRA) was established in order to regulate the supply of natural rubber. With a view to achieving that goal, surplus stocks would have to be reduced to a normal level and for that, regulation of production and export was considered necessary. By the Agreement, quotas were assigned to each participating country roughly on the basis of the average exports from 1929 to 1932. In order to prevent further expansion of production capacity, new planting was prohibited, except for experimental purposes at one quarter of one per cent of the total area. Replanting was also strictly limited. A local Committee was appointed in 1934 for the enforcement of the Regulation, the 'Indian Rubber Licensing Committee' The International Rubber Regulation Scheme was in operation in India from 1934 to 1942 only.

By 1942 the situation in India had changed drastically. The conquest of Malaya and other South East Asian countries by Japan left the Allied Nations with India and Ceylon for obtaining rubber. This situation brought about a complete transformation in the prospect of rubber plantation in India. In 1942 the Government of India issued the Rubber Stocks (Control) Order under which the estates, dealers and manufacturers were required to submit returns on stocks to the Government. Further the Government of India converted the maximum prices of rubber into fixed prices. The Government also removed all restrictions imposed on planting of rubber and the rubber growers were encouraged to maximise production. As a result a spurt in planting activities occurred between 1943 and 1946.

On 30 September 1946 the above measures expired. However, the rubber growers who knew that the assurance of a steady price and regulated growth would then be affected, had in the meanwhile convened a conference to discuss the situation. The conference recommended to the Government of India that a permanent organisation should be set up to develop the rubber plantation sector in India on scientific lines. On the basis of the recommendations of the growers, the Government of India decided to set up the Rubber Board of India to look after the development of the rubber industry.

1.3 The development of the natural rubber sector since independence

In 1949 the area under rubber plantation in India registered by the Rubber Board was 67,915 ha. Table 1.1 shows the size distribution of the area among smallholders and estates. From the table it can be seen that 60.3% of the total area was owned by estates of 40 ha. and above. The estates of between 20 ha. and 40 ha. accounted for 7.9% of the total area. The total area of smallholdings of 20 ha. and below was 31.8%.The geographical distribution of rubber area in India in 1949 is given in Figure 1.1, showing that the erstwhile Travancore State had 72.9% of the area under rubber plan. If Travancore, Cochin and Madras are taken together, the percentage would be 97.6.

Table 1.1: Distribution of area under rubber in India in 1949

Size of estates/holdings	Number	Area (ha)	Percentage of total area
Estates			
above 40 ha.	249	40,933	60.3
from 20 ha. to 40 ha.	198	5,392	7.9
Smallholdings			
from 4 ha. to 20 ha.	1,277	9,802	14.4
from 0.4 ha. to 4 ha.	9,703	11,228	16.5
below 0.4 ha.	2,416	560	0.8
Total	13,843	67,915	100.0

Note: Area refers to the extent registered with the Rubber Board only.
Source: Rubber Board, Kottayam, South India.

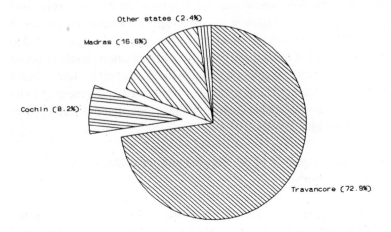

Figure 1.1: Geographical distribution of rubber area in India, 1949

Notes: Other states comprise Coorg, Andamans, Mysore and Assam.
          Area refers to the extent registered with the Rubber Board only.
Source: Rubber Board, Kottayam, South India.

The Replanting Subsidy Scheme, which was the first major development scheme taken up, was launched in 1957. Five years later a modest scheme for giving interest-free loan assistance to smallholders for expanding their rubber holdings to viable units by new planting was introduced. This was followed by a package of measures to popularise scientific cultivation and production of rubber with technical assistance and limited financial support. The rates of replanting subsidy introduced in 1957 were revised in 1960, in 1975 and again in 1980 taking into account the escalation in cost of planting and maintenance. The rubber plantation sector reacted positively to the various measures and under the favourable combination of the then prevailing socio-economic conditions, price protection and research assisted development, all round growth and improvement were achieved during the decades that followed.

During the 1950s and 1960s, large scale expansion of rubber cultivation took place as a consequence of the move in Kerala State for imposition of a ceiling on landholdings from which rubber plantations along with other plantations were exempted, prevalence of steady and remunerative price for rubber, diversion of extensive areas under disease infected coconut plantations in Central Kerala to rubber plantation, etc. Intensification of R&D programmes by the Rubber Board during this period also contributed to the increase in production of rubber. As a cumulative effect of these, production of rubber picked up appreciably. The average growth in NR production during 1950s was 4.4% per year and in 1960s it improved to 13.1% per year. Substantial increase in smallholdings took place during the period 1955-56 to 1962-63. This was partly due to the fact that during those years agrarian reforms were on the anvil. The legislation had proposed to exempt rubber and other plantation crops from the purview of land-ceiling. Accordingly there was a rush to convert other areas into rubber plantation. The plantations started by the Government of Kerala, Tamil Nadu and Karnataka had resulted in a substantial increase in the area of estates during the 1960s.

As a result of the fall in the growth rate of consumption during the 1970s due to the general industrial recession, domestic supply was in excess of demand and it resulted in a crash in prices. The uncertain market conditions during the 1970s created gloom and pessimism amongst growers and it had resulted in a fall in planting activities. During the 1970s the area newly planted fell to 52,000 ha. from 82,000 ha. in 1960s. As the rubber tree takes about 7 years to start giving yield, the fall in the planting tempo had resulted in a set back in production during 1978-79 to 1984-85 and the country resumed imports from 1978-79.

1.4 Planting schemes and production during the 1980s

Given the projected shortfall in natural rubber supply in the years to come, an intensive rubber production drive was launched for stepping up the rubber production. In 1979-80, for the first time a subsidy-cum-credit scheme was introduced on a pilot basis for encouraging new planting. Noticing the excellent response to the scheme, an integrated scheme known as 'Rubber Plantation Development Scheme' (RPD) was launched in 1980-81 for accelerating new planting and replanting. The following forms of assistance were provided to the growers under the scheme during the VI Five Year Plan period (1980-81 to 1984-85):

a)   subsidy at the rate of Rs. 5,000/ha. to rubber growers owning up to 20 ha. and Rs. 3,000/ha. to rubber growers owning above 20 ha.;

b)   additional assistance to smallholders owning up to 6 ha. by way of reimbursement of the cost of planting materials, half of the cost of fertilisers applied during the immaturity period and a subsidy of Rs. 150/ha. for soil conservation work.

When the scheme was introduced the cost of planting and maintenance up to tapping stage was Rs. 15,000/ha. The subsidy and additional assistance then covered about 50% of the cost of planting and maintenance. The growers who availed loans from financial institutions to bridge the planting cost, were given financial assistance by the Board by means of an interest subsidy at the rate of 3% on such loans. During the VII Plan period (1984-85 to 1989-90) the cash subsidy rate was restricted to smallholders owning up to 5 ha. in traditional areas and to all growers in non-traditional areas. The additional assistance given was confined to the use of planting materials of poly-bagged plants of advanced growth up to a maximum of Rs. 2,700/ha. The interest subsidy of 3% was also restricted to smallholders owning up to 5 ha. in traditional areas and to all growers in non-traditional areas. The planting and maintenance cost during 1985-86 was Rs. 22,000/ha. The financial assistance then granted by the Board covered only 35% of the cost of planting and maintenance cost.

In 1955-56, there were 446 estates which occupied 55.3% of the total planted area. In 1991-92 the corresponding figures were 343 and 16.0%. The drastic decline in the share of the estates in the total planted area was due to the favourable policies for smallholders as compared to estates. In 1955-56 there were 29,587 smallholdings with a planted area of 38,488 ha. while in 1991-92 the corresponding figures were over 800,000 and 410,222 ha.

The rubber plantation sector has made many strides since

independence. The production of natural rubber which was only 15,394 tonnes in 1948-49 increased to 366,745 by 1991-92. Similarly the yield per hectare which was only 320 kg. in 1948-49 increased to 1130 kg. by 1991-92. The yield per hectare was lower in Karnataka (985 kg.) while it was higher in Tamil Nadu (1147 kg.) and Kerala (1142 kg.) in 1991-92. During the period 1940 to 1950 the production of natural rubber in India remained more or less static at about 16,000 tonnes per annum. During the year 1950-51 the production of natural rubber was 15,830 tonnes of which 3,387 tonnes were produced in the smallholdings (21.4%). The share of smallholdings has increased rapidly with the increase in their area and reached 302,700 tonnes (82.5%) out of 366,745 tonnes produced in 1991-92.

1.5 The geographical and organizational distribution of natural rubber growing area

The geographical distribution of rubber growing area has not changed much over the years. Rubber was cultivated mainly in erstwhile Travancore, Cochin and the Malabar districts of Madras State in 1949. Together these areas formed almost the whole of the Kerala State and even after about forty years, planting of rubber still continues to be concentrated in that State. The geographical and organizational distribution of the rubber growing area in 1991-92 is given in Table 1.2.

Rubber plantations in India operate with certain inherent infirmities which can be summarised as below:

a) Rubber trees grow and yield best in the equable climate of tropical equatorial regions lying within 10 degree North and South latitudes. In India, only about 50% of the total planted area comes within this ideal location. The remaining area experience rather inhospitable conditions to varying degrees. These result in extensive disease incidence, occurrence of droughts, prolongation of gestation period, loss of tapping days due to continuous and heavy rain and, as a cumulative result of all these, a relatively high cost of production. Abnormal leaf-fall disease caused by the intensity of rainfall is controlled by

Table 1.2: Geographical distribution of rubber growing area (ha.) in India, 1991-1992

States	Holdings	Estates	Total
Kerala	373,696	45,478	419,174
Tamil Nadu	9,996	7,214	17,210
Karnataka	7,531	6,855	14,386
A & N Islands	68	896	964
Tripura	8,518	9,342	17,860
Assam	7,288	2,452	9,740
Meghalaya	1,183	2,875	4,058
Nagaland	564	780	1,344
Mizoram	123	837	960
Manipur	437	778	1,215
Goa	405	573	978
Maharashtra	18	132	150
Orissa	217	80	297
Andhra Pradesh	178		178
Total	410,222	78,292	488,514

Source: Rubber Board, Kottayam, South India

prophylactic spraying of fungicides. Rain guarding of rubber trees is to be carried out to enable tapping during the rainy season. The cost of these two operations is estimated to be around Rs. 2000 per hectare, which is not necessary in most other countries;

b) Topography-wise also lands planted in India are relatively more steep, or undulating. This not only reduces labour productivity, but also increases the general cost of cultivation and maintenance. The simplest form of contour terracing costs Rs. 3000 per hectare;

c) Structurally, 84% of the total area smallholders numbering over 800,000 who contribute 82% of the production. The average size of a smallholder is only 0.50 ha. In order to be effective planning for development should largely aim at modernisation of cultivation, production and marketing in the smallholding sector. The structure of the sector makes diffusion of modern technologies difficult.

Rubber is grown mainly in Kerala State and the adjoining Kanyakumari District of Tamil Nadu State. Together these form the traditional rubber growing region in the country. Scope for further expansion in traditional area is very limited as already almost all the available area has been put under various crops. Experimental and trial plantations carried out in the 1960s and the 1970s revealed that large scale expansion of rubber cultivation can be undertaken successfully in selected other parts of the country such as vast stretches of areas in the North East region, Andaman and Nicobar Islands, Goa, southern parts of Konkan region of Maharashtra State, certain parts of Orissa and Andhra Pradesh, Bastar District of Madhya Pradesh and certain parts of West Bengal. The cost of cultivation and maintenance of rubber in these marginal areas is relatively low on account of availability of comparatively low cost labour. The low yield potential of these areas, which is estimated to be 80% of the traditional areas, would be to a great extent compensated by reduced cost of cultivation. Rubber plantations respond well in growth and yield to irrigation during dry months. Therefore, wherever irrigation is possible in marginal tracts, the same could be judiciously used to make rubber cultivation successful. The adverse effects of climatic conditions can also be overcome to a great extent by selection of planting materials and adoption of cultural practices suited to each location.

Apart from the climatic limitations the other constraints faced in expanding rubber cultivation in non-traditional areas are

a) poor state of infrastructural facilities;
b) lack of awareness of the benefits of rubber cultivation and of the methods of rubber cultivation and production;
c) difficulties in making available the required inputs like planting materials, fertilisers, fungicides etc.; and
d) problems with regard to land tenure systems, especially in tribal areas.

Given these constraints special projects were prepared and launched during the VI Plan period to develop infrastructural facilities etc. The project thus introduced in 1984 for the North Eastern region covered the establishment of a research complex, strengthening of the Board's organisational machinery for developmental and extension work and, finally, establishment of a large farm [Nucleus Rubber Estate & Training Centre (NRETC)] for training and demonstration. The target was to plant 24,000 ha. during 1984 to 1989 in the North East region under the project. This has been achieved. An NRETC is functioning in Andaman and Nicobar Islands from 1986. A project approved in 1988 for the development of Eastern India comprising Orissa, Andhra Pradesh, Madhya Pradesh and West Bengal is also being implemented. The ground work done in the North East and other nontraditional areas during the VI and VII Plans would facilitate large scale development in the coming years. The statistics in Table 1.3 depict the progress in expansion of rubber cultivation in non- traditional areas *vis-a-vis* in traditional areas.

Over the years, the Indian Rubber Plantation Sector has undergone remarkable structural changes. Up to 1955-56 the area under estates of above 20 ha. was higher than of smallholders (up to and including 20 ha.). During 1956-57 the area under smallholdings exceeded that of the estates. Since then the extent under smallholdings increased steadily and by 1979-80, 75% of the area under rubber was in smallholdings sector. By 1991-92 it went up to 84%. For detailed structural breakups see Table 1.4 below.

Table 1.3: Planting in traditional and non-traditional areas (ha.)

	VI Plan	VII Plan
Traditional	81,000	65,000
Non-traditional	8,000	25,000
Total	89,000	90,000

Table 1.4: Structure of rubber plantations

	1979-80		1991-92	
	No. of units	Area in ha.	No. of Units	Area in ha.
Estates				
Government owned corporations/departments	28	20,600	52	40,722
Limited Companies	126	28,700	101	26,871
Socio-religious organisations	28	1,719	25	1,635
Individuals & partnerships	300	15,271	165	9,064
Estates total	482	66,290 (25%)	343	78,292 (16%)
Smallholdings*	175,000	195,100 (75%)	800,000	410,222 (84%)
Total*	176,000	261,000	800,000	488,514

(*Rounded)

A perspective plan has been prepared by the Board with a view to achieve self-sufficiency in NR. Details will be presented in Chapter 10.

1.6 Targets and performance of natural rubber planting and replanting under past Five-year Plans

No targets were fixed for the First and Second Five-Year Plans for rubber. Targets *vis-a-vis* achievements during the subsequent plans are presented in Table 1.5. The table shows a mixed overall performance. During the IV and the V Five-Year Plans the achievements lagged behind the targets in replanting and during the IV Plan in new planting as well. Especially in the Fourth Plan the difference is huge; in case of replanting less than 50% of the target was realised, while in case of new planting around 60% was realised. This was mainly due to the steep fall in price during the 1970s due to poor demand for rubber as already

explained. On the other hand, during both the VI and especially, the VII
Five-Year Plan an enormous increase is seen in new planting.

Table 1.5: Targets and achievements during plan periods

Five-Year Plan	Targets			Achievements		
	New Planting (in ha.)	Replanting (in ha.)	Production (in tonnes)	New Planting (in ha.)	Replanting (in ha.)	Production (in tonnes)
III	20,235	18,214	45,000	26,000	14,100	50,530
IV	39,000	20,000	125,000	24,000	9,000	125,153
V	25,000	20,000	not fixed	27,000	16,200	
VI	30,000	30,000	192,000	53,200	19,500	186,450
VII	30,000	10,000	265,000	51,000	23,500	297,000

Note: Production refers to the terminal year of the Plan while newplanting and
replanting refer to the aggregate over the Five-Year Period.
The Five-Year Plans covers the following period:
III 1961-62 to 1965-66;
IV 1969-70 to 1973-74;
V 1974-75 to 1978-79;
VI 1980-81 to 1984-85;
VII 1985-86 to 1989-90.
During the VI and VII Plan, targets and achievements of newplanting and
replanting refer to the extent brought under the Rubber Plantation Development
Scheme with subsidy. Area planted without subsidy is not taken into account.

The reasons for the shortfall in replanting during VI Plan were
identified as follows:
a) rubber price ruled fairly high during the period as a result of
    which smallholders were reluctant to cut away their trees
    which, despite a low yield, were still capable of giving a
    sizeable income at the prevailing prices;
b) the importance of replanting had got side-tracked in the face of
    extensive new planting; Rubber Board's officials in the field,
    limited as they were in number, had to devote their main
    attention to reviewing applications at hand so much so that any
    large scale move for canvassing for replanting was not possible
    VII Five-Year Plan.

The total new planted area during the 1980s including the extent brought outside the RPD-Scheme was 199,000 ha. as against 57,000 ha. in the 1970s. The financial incentive granted for new planting and replanting during the 7th Plan period was continued during 1990-91 and 1991-92.

The analysis relating supply to area is given in Chapter 6. The targets for new planting and replanting are presented in Chapter 10. These targets and alternative scenarios will be assessed in Part IV of this report when the full analysis on supply, demand and prices is complete and projections and policy simulations are presented.

2

THE SYNTHETIC RUBBER INDUSTRY

2.1 Introduction

Commercial production and use of synthetic rubber (SR) started in many countries during the Second World War. However, production and use of this rubber in India started rather late in the 1950s and on a very limited level. Even by 1955-56 the consumption of SR in the country increased only to 461 tonnes or 1.6% of the total rubber consumption (NR and SR). Thereafter, it improved gradually and rose to 10,723 tonnes by 1962-63 giving a share of SR of 16.7%. In the past decades the share of SR in total rubber consumption has always been close to 20%. This chapter gives a review of the synthetic rubber industry.

2.2 The producers

Up to 1962-63 the entire demand for SR in the country was met by imports. Production of SR started in India in 1963. During the year, a plant established by M/s. Synthetics & Chemicals Ltd., a public limited company, started production of Ethyl Alcohol based Styrene Butadiene Synthetic Rubber (SBR) in Uttar Pradesh (North India). At that time there were no petrochemical complexes in the country and the Uttar Pradesh State Sugar Mills had abundance of alcohol, which they distilled out of molasses, a by-product of sugar production. M/s. Synthetics & Chemicals took up this alcohol and converted it into Butadiene and Styrene in two separate captive plants and set up two more plants, one for latex and the other for rubber to copolymerize them into SBR. The peculiar circumstances then prevailing in the country made for the selection of alcohol as the basic raw-material. The process was then discarded as obsolete in western countries. With the possible exemption of one unit in Brazil, every other known producer in the world was by then using naphtha instead, for manufacturing SBR. The factory would produce SBR out of petro- feed stocks also.

The main grades produced by the company were:

a) general purpose staining (S-1500 grade) and non-staining (S-1502 grade);

b) general usage staining oil extended (S-1712 grade);

c) non-staining reinforced rubber specially required by footwear (S-1958 grade).

Since 1970 the company has not produced S-1500 grade. They are also marketing small quantities of SBR latex since 1974. During the period from 1973 to 1980 very limited quantities of Nitrile Rubber (NBR) were also produced by the company. The initial installed capacity of the factory was 30,000 tonnes of SBR and 2,000 tonnes of NBR per annum.

The second SR factory, owned by the Indian Petro Chemicals Corporation Ltd., a public sector undertaking of the Government of India, started commercial production in 1978. It was established in collaboration with M/s. Polysar Ltd., Canada. The installed capacity of the factory was 20,000 tonnes of Poly Butadiene Rubber (BR) per annum. In addition to the above two factories, two small factories were also producing SR viz., M/s. APAR (P) Ltd., and M/s. Asian Paints (India) Ltd. The first factory started production of High Styrene self reinforcing rubber (SBR) in 1988 for the footwear industry with an installed capacity of 3,000 tonnes per year. The second factory is producing Vinyl Pyridine rubber latex, SBR latex and Nitrile rubber latex since 1989 with a total installed capacity of around 2,000 tonnes per year. During 1991-92 one small factory established by M/s. Gujarath Apar Ltd. with a capacity of 6,250 tonnes, started production of nitrile rubber. The total production of all factories during 1991-92 was 57,000 tonnes.

2.3 Developments in demand for the various types of SR

At the start the production of SBR was very low due to consumer resistance to the new product and initial teething troubles. The price was initially 25% higher than the price of NR. So the company faced difficulties in marketing the rubber and approached the government for special assistance in creating favourable conditions. Consequently the government interceded and advised the major rubber consumers, particularly the tyre companies, to lift certain specific quantities of SBR. A link was also established between the off-take of allotted quantities of SBR and import requirements of balance quantities of NR and special purpose SRS. As a corollary, the producer of SBR agreed to a voluntary price control on the product. The price thus arrived at was revised from time to time giving relief to the company for increased cost of production and to ensure a fair return on the capital employed by them.

The use of SR, both in absolute and relative terms increased steadily up to 1971-72 when it touched 37,209 tonnes or 27.8% of the rubber consumption. In the subsequent two years, the consumption recorded a steep fall and thereafter it picked up gradually and only in 1978-79 it exceeded the level attained in 1971-72. During the period, the supply of SR was short of the demand and at the same time the supply of NR was in excess of the demand mainly due to the slow-down in growth in demand owing to the spurt in the oil prices and consequent developments. During the period price support operations had been carried out for NR including export of small quantities. The relative use of SR during 1972-73 and 1973-74 fell to a very low level of 15.5%. Since 1978-79, both supply and demand for SR picked up and by 1991-92 the production of all varieties of SR was 57,000 tonnes and consumption 105,650 tonnes. The deficit between production and consumption was met by imports. Imports comprised mostly Butyl Rubber (IIR), SBR, BR and limited quantities of Nitrile (NBR), Polychloroprene (CR) and VP latex. Customs duty is levied on imported rubber mainly to protect the local producers. The pattern of usage of different varieties of SR was as shown in Table 2.1. The consumption pattern by end-use in shown in detail in Chapters 7 and 8. In summary: about 50% is used for automotive tyres and tubes, 10% for cycle tyres and tubes, 20% for footwear and the remaining 20% for the various other applications.

2.4 The peculiar situation of NR/SR in India

The relative use of SR during the 1980s varied within a very narrow range of 22% and 23% and it was much below the level of 27.8% touched in 1971-72. Currently consumption of SR and NR in India is in the ratio of 22:78 as against a global pattern of use of 65:35. Unlike other

Table 2.1: Consumption of different tyres of SR (tonnes)

	1970-71	1980-81	1990-91	1991-92
SBR	28,118	25,125	45,225	44,035
	(84.8%)	(53.4%)	(43.2%)	(41.7%)
BR	577	7,150	27,115	27,430
	(1.7%)	(15.2%)	(25.9%)	(26.0%)
Butyl	2,702	8,410	20,884	21,793
	(8.1%)	(17.9%)	(19.9%)	(20.6%)
Polychloroprene	460	950	2,941	3,065
	(1.4%)	(2.0%)	(2.8%)	(2.9%)
Nitrile	530	1,103	3,580	3,573
	(1.6%)	(2.3%)	(3.4%)	(3.4%)
Latex	673	2,035	3,210	3,570
	(2.0%)	(4.3%)	(3.1%)	(3.4%)
Others@	100	2,275	1,780	2,184
	(0.3%)	(4.8%)	(1.7%)	(2.1%)
Total	33,160	47,050	104,735	105,650

@ Out of which EPDM: 600 tonnes in 1990-91 and 680 tonnes in 1991-92

leading rubber consuming countries, India has a strong NR production base. The policy of the government was to increase the production of NR and only a supplementary role was given to SR production in meeting the demand due to socio-economic reasons. The reasons for this are as follows:

a) **Capital costs**: Compared to the SR industry, the NR plantation sector is less capital intensive. No foreign exchange or import of know-how is involved in developing rubber plantations as are required in the case of establishing SR capacity. To establish a factory producing 50,000 tonnes of SBR, it is estimated that a massive investment of Rs. 500-600 crores will be needed. At least 25% of this will be in hard currency. For producing 50,000 tonnes of SBR about 80,000 tonnes of naphtha will have to be imported and cracked to produce the monomers required for polymerisation. Some of the initiators, polymer stabilisers etc. may also have to be imported. In contrast to this for producing 50,000 tonnes of NR the investment required is only around

Rs. 120 crores, on the assumption that the yield will be 1,500 kg/
ha. and the planting and maintenance cost up to the trapping
stage is Rs. 40,000/ha.

b) **Production costs**: The high cost of production is attributed to
the scarcity and high cost of raw materials and increased duties
and taxes. The minimum economic size of an SR factory in
Indian conditions is 100,000 tonnes according to the Press Note
issued by the Government of India (Ministry of Industry) in
August 1989. Against this the existing capacities of the two big
factories may be another reason for the high cost of production.
An excise duty is levied on the SR produced in the country since
March 1970. Initially the rate was Rs. 300 per tonne. The rate
is 1991-92 was 15.75% of the price.

c) **Energy and environment**: Rubber plantations being about the
much needed ecological restoration of the countryside and
supply fuel wood, timber, vegetable oil, oil cake and honey as
by-products. Rubber plantations are renewable and non-
polluting. The SR production requires costly energy inputs
while the rubber plantations produce rubber as a result of
photosynthetic action in nature. Most of the areas considered fit
for rubber cultivation are already badly denuded as a result of
indiscriminate shifting cultivation. By growing rubber on such
lands they can be regenerated and the economically backward
tribals and others weaned towards settled agriculture.

d) **Employment**: SR plants generate much less employment
opportunities than what NR plantations can generate. One
hectare rubber plantation gives employment to 0.7 person.

e) **End-uses**: around 45% of the rubber in the country is used for
manufacturing auto tyres and tubes. In this sector, around 70%
of the production of tyres in terms of tonnage is large size truck
and bus tyres, whereas passenger car tyre production
predominates in the developed countries. For the production of
bus and truck tyres, NR is preferred all over the world.

3

THE RECLAIMED RUBBER INDUSTRY

3.1 Introduction

The use of reclaimed rubber (RR) is as old as natural rubber (NR). In the past decades the share of RR in total rubber consumption in India has always been close to 10%. This chapter aims at describing the supply side of reclaimed rubber, then presenting some insight in the technical properties of reclaimed rubber and finally discussing consumption aspects.

3.2 The supply of reclaimed rubber

By the early part of this century the reclaimed rubber industry had established itself. However, the reclaimed rubber industry began to disappear in the industrialised countries after 1960. Part of the reason can be attributed to the emergence of a strong synthetic rubber industry in the industrialised countries. Although this is the picture in the industrialised countries, reclaimed rubber units were set up in India only in the early 1960s, although small quantities were produced by important rubber goods manufacturers for their own use in their factories. In the second half of the eighties, there were 32 reclaimed rubber factories in India. But nine of them were closed down in the subsequent years. The consumption data for reclaimed rubber are available from the year 1952-53 and in that year around 2000 tonnes of reclaimed rubber was consumed in India. Before 1960-61 substantial quantities of reclaimed rubber were imported.

At the end of 1990 the number of factories producing reclaimed rubber, according to the Indian Rubber Reclaimers' Association, was 35. The break up of the factories is given in Table 3.1. It can be seen from which that more units are located in the south. However, more reclaimed rubber is consumed in the Northern Zone. The installed capacity and the

Table 3.1: Number of factories at the beginning of the year

	1991-92
Western zone	3
Eastern zone	2
Southern zone	15
Northern zone	15
Total	35

Note: Western Zone - Gujarat and Maharashtra
        Eastern Zone - West Bengal
        Southern Zone - Kerala, Tamil Nadu, Karnataka and Andhra Pradesh
        Northern Zone - Delhi, Haryana, Punjab and U.P.

production of the reclaimed rubber industry are presented in Table 3.2. The percentage of capacity utilization in 1991-92 was 64%.

In 1990-91 a study was conducted by the Rubber Board to find out the current position of the reclaimed rubber industry in India. Data could be collected from 22 units. Of the 22 units covered by the study, 15 units were operated by public limited companies, 6 units by private limited companies and remaining one was a partnership firm. Of the 22 units, four units were in existence before 1970 and 18 units started after 1970. In addition there were a few units producing powder from discarded rubber products. Part of the powder was sold to the reclaimed rubber units. However, such units are not included in the total, as they are not full fledged reclaimed rubber producing units. All the 22 units, except one operated on a three shift basis. The industry employed around 2000 persons directly.

Table 3.2: Capacity and production

Installed capacity of the units	Production (fiscal years)		
	1989-90	1990-91	1991-92
85,000 tonnes	47,615	53,629	54,185

3.3 The technical side of the industry

Technically reclaimed rubber is obtained from ground vulcanised scrap rubber. This is achieved by replasticisation (depolymerisation) using heat or pressure or both and chemical agents. There are certain advantages in the use of reclaimed rubber as it assists the mixing, extruding and calendering processes. Because of the processing, the plasticity is considerably reduced and it comes in the moving range of 35-40, and mixing is reduced. The other advantages are less shrinkage during extrusion and calendering, more stable extrusion and less chances of over cure. By saving the mixing time, power consumption is also reduced. To an extent reclaimed rubber gives the compound improved shape and stability. As a result, the cost of production is reduced. However, there are some disadvantages to reclaimed rubber as it decreases tensile strength, modulus, resilience, tear resistance and abrasion resistance.

There are different types of reclaimed rubber. The most important is the whole tyre reclaim. It is produced from whole tyres containing about 45 to 50 per cent of rubber hydro-carbon. Then there is the minimum straining reclaim; the reduction in straining characteristics is achieved by the use of activated carbon and non-staining oils. The third is drab and coloured reclaim; it is made from non-black scrap. The fourth is butyl reclaim; the raw material for this reclaimed rubber is the butyl inner tubes. All these types of reclaimed rubber are produced in India.

The main raw material for the industry is of course the scrap rubber. However, tyre buffings, latex products' waste and chappal wastes are also used by the units in India. Other raw-materials are chemicals, mineral oil and fillers. Some of these items are imported and the average import component by value was 12% in 1990.

Reclaimed rubber has been classified mainly into four grades viz. superfine, fine, medium and coarse, with some of them having a few sub-grades. Table 3.3 shows the prices of these grades. Superfine is potentially the highest from the price point of view. The percentage of production of these grades for the industry as a whole was estimated at 25, 25, 30 and 15 respectively the balance of 5 per cent accounted for other grades.

Table 3.3: Grade-wise price 1990 (Rs.)

	Super	Fine	Medium	Coarse
Maximum price	8.25	7.70	7.10	5.50
Minimum price	6.50	6.10	6.60	4.50

3.4 Consumption of reclaimed rubber

Although in India, natural, synthetic and reclaimed rubber are all used, the progressive increase in the consumption of these varieties is not on an even keel. Table 3.4 gives production and consumption of reclaimed rubber since 1960-61.

Reclaimed rubber is used in many applications. Table 3.5 shows the articles for which reclaimed rubber is being used as well as the percentage each type of article has in the market. While battery boxes consist for a large part of reclaimed rubber, the most important product for which reclaimed rubber is used is cycle tyres and tubes which automobile tyres and tubes also consume considerable quantities of it.

Table 3.4: Production and consumption of reclaimed rubber, at five-year intervals and in recent years

Year	Production	Consumption
1960-61	2,000	5,453
1964-65	9,500	9,369
1969-70	15,507	14,255
1974-75	19,581	18,096
1979-80	29,336	25,660
1984-85	39,195	34,625
1990-91	53,629	52,500
1991-92	54,185	54,015

Source: Rubber Board

Table 3.5: Consumption of reclaimed rubber by end-use, 1991-92

Type of products for which reclaimed rubber is used	Consumption (tonnes)	Percentage to total
Cycle tyres and tubes	17,545	32.5
Battery boxes	8,452	15.6
Auto tyres and tubes @	7,738	14.3
Footwear	6,750	12.5
Moulded goods	5,850	10.8
Belts and hoses	3,660	6.8
Tread rubber	3,450	6.4
Others	570	1.1
Total	54,015	100.0

@ Including animal drawn vehicles, tractors off-the-road etc.

There are some additional advantages when reclaimed rubber is used. Reclaimed rubber is recovered from discarded tyres. These tyres would have otherwise created ecological problems in the neighborhood. An amount of pollution control is also achieved by recycling the discarded tyres. If the recycling is not done, either new natural or synthetic rubber will have to be used in its place. To that extent resources are conserved by the industry. All over India discarded tyres are available in plenty. These tyres are non-perishable and become a fire and health hazard. Fortunately during the last thirty years, almost the entire discarded tyres are utilised in India, most of them being processed into reclaimed rubber. Besides recycling discarded tyres into reclaimed rubber, a certain amount of metal and other residues are recovered from them. The metal beads in the tyres are purchased by steel industries to augment their raw material supply. Fibre obtained from the tyres is used in some areas for running tube wells or drawing water from the wells. Discarded tyres are also used as dock fenders and for the sole of low quality footwear.

Although the reclaimed rubber industry used mainly discarded tyres, the buffings from rubber retreading factories and rubber factory rejects are also used as raw materials. Rejected gloves and other goods from latex also form a small part of the raw material base.

Part II
Analysis of Natural Rubber Supply

4

THE SUPPLY OF NATURAL RUBBER: RESULTS OF A SURVEY

4.1 Introduction

A sample field survey was undertaken with a view to ascertaining the smallholder's attitude towards replanting, newplanting and market prices, choice of alternative crops, tapping systems etc. Smallholders are rubber growers owning 20 ha. or less. In this chapter the answers to the questions asked to the farmers are summarized. In the following chapter the information obtained is translated into a model of farmer behaviour at the micro-level. At the level of policy making, however, it is the aggregate of India that counts. A macro-model comprising the aggregate of all rubber farmers in India is developed in Chapter 6 with features of and assumptions on farmers' behaviour as could be derived from the micro-model in Chapter 5.

The questionnaire for eliciting the information from smallholders (see Appendix D) was designed by the Rubber Board in consultation with the Economic and Social Institute. A sample of 4,400 smallholders was selected employing a stratified random sampling technique. Rubber growing *taluks* (revenue divisions) were selected as the strata. The entire traditional rubber growing area is spread over 55 *taluks*. The smallholders in the traditional rubber growing region cover 94% of the total area of the category in the country. The field work was carried out from 22nd June 1992 to the middle of July 1992. For this work, 250 enumerators were recruited from the educated unemployed. They were given exhaustive training on collection of data, filling in of the questionnaire etc. for a period of three days. In doubtful cases, the filled in questionnaires were checked again by the Statistical Inspectors of the Rubber Board. Eventually, 4,000 filled in questionnaires were utilised for processing as reliable information could not be collected from some of the holders due to the absence of the owner at the time of the visit, or lack of reliable data due to transactions of the holdings etc. The work was carried out under the guidance and supervision of the Statistics and Planning Division of the Rubber Board.

4.2 Characterisation of the rubber producers

The 4,000 households consist of a total of 17,647 persons, 4.4 persons on average. The majority of the heads of the households have farming as main occupation, but many report other occupations. Of all persons in the households who have a job, 47% claim to be farmers, and the majority has non-farming activities as the main occupation, among which government service is mentioned most frequently. Table 4.1 gives details.

Table 4.1: Main occupation of household heads and all members with a job

	household no.	heads percent	all no.	occupied persons percent
Government servant	386	10	1150	19
Farmer	2160	54	2753	47
Coolie	217	5	446	8
Self-employed	241	6	470	8
Private com employee	77	2	328	6
Others	321	8	736	12
No indication	598	15		
Total	4000	100	5883	100

The educational status of the household heads is reflected in Table 4.2 that lists the numbers of household heads by educational training received.

Table 4.2: Educational status of household heads

	No.	Percent		No.	Percent
illiterate	141	3.5	profession	1 62	1.5
below sslc	2134	53.4	technical	46	1.1
sslc	1116	27.9	pre-degree	172	4.3
graduation	227	5.7	others	32	0.8
post graduate	59	1.5	no indication	11	0.3

Table 4.3 shows the way in which the farmers have become rubber cultivators. Most are first generation cultivators, having purchased or created rubber area rather than having inherited it. Still about a quarter became rubber cultivator by inheritance.

Table 4.3: Ways of becoming rubber cultivator

Way	number of observations	percent
Inheritance	1026	25.6
Purchasing	1493	37.3
Planted in fresh land	322	8.1
Removing other crop	1019	25.5
Multiple or no answer	140	3.5
Total	4000	100.0

Table 4.4 gives an indication of the levels of income from various sources. Although all households grow rubber, only 2879 families (i.e. 72%) reported to have rubber cultivation as a source of income. This low percentage is partly due to the fact that many households own rubber areas with immature trees only. Not surprisingly, in view of Table 4.1, 3178 families reported to have sources of income other than agriculture. Summed over all households, average income per household is Rs. 28,571, consisting of Rs. 11,343 from rubber growing, Rs. 3,448 from other crops, Rs. 8,762 from employment and Rs. 5,018 from other sources. Most households have more than one source of income: the

most frequent combinations are rubber and other crops (18.0%); rubber, other crops and 'other' income (14.8%); rubber, other crops and employment (12.8%) and other crops plus 'other' income (9.7%). In only 7.5% of all cases is rubber the only source of income. The share that income from rubber takes in total income can vary from zero to 100%, and its distribution is fairly equal: disregarding households without income from rubber, in 23% of the remaining households, rubber constitutes less than 30% of all income, in 45% of the households rubber forms less than half of total income and in 71% of the households rubber constitutes less than 80% of total income.

Table 4.4: Family income by source

Source	Number of observations	Average income (Rs.)
Rubber	2,879	15,759
Other crops	2,715	5,080
Employment	1,361	25,750
Others	1,817	11,048

4.3 Rubber area and production

Area

The total area under rubber of the households in the sample was 2837 hectares, or 0.71 hectares per households on average. The size distribution of the rubber area over the households is given in Table 4.5. Without exception, all persons interviewed can be considered as smallholders. More than 50% of all households cultivated a total rubber area smaller than 0.5 hectare, and less than 25% owned rubber plots larger than 1 hectare.

As rubber is a perennial crop, the existing rubber area is composed of trees planted as long ago as 30 years. Figure 4.1 shows how the rubber plantation area was composed in 1992. It shows for example that out of the present 2837 hectares, 167 ha. have been planted in 1991, and that

Table 4.5: Area cultivated with rubber in 1992

Area (ha.)	Number of households	Percentage
≤ 0.25	785	19.6
0.25-0.50	1256	31.4
0.50-0.75	625	15.6
0.75-1.00	526	13.2
1.00-1.25	288	7.2
1.25-1.50	144	3.6
1.50-1.75	121	3.0
1.75-2.00	91	2.3
2.00-2.50	68	1.7
2.50-3.00	48	1.2
3.00-8.00	48	1.2
Total	4000	100.0

no rubber trees exist that have been planted before 1955. All results in this section concerning the years of planting from 1955 until 1963 must be treated with caution, as the number of observed plots from these years is less than 5. Figure 4.1 shows that of the existing trees many have been planted in the beginning of the 1980s, while planting has diminished in more recent years. Figure 4.2 presents the composition of the total rubber plantation area by age groups, each age group consisting of 7 years. As can readily be seen, no less than 29.3% is still immature, while only 7.1% is older than 20 years. The average area per household under rubber plantation is 0.71 ha. It can be considered the average of three statistics: the average area under rubber plantation (0.58 ha) of 1117 households having only immature trees, the average area under rubber plantation (0.65 ha) of 2181 households having only mature trees and the average area under rubber plantation (1.10 ha) of 702 households having both mature and immature trees.

Production

The length of the immaturity period can be found in Figure 4.3, which shows the average age at which the tree is opened by year of planting.

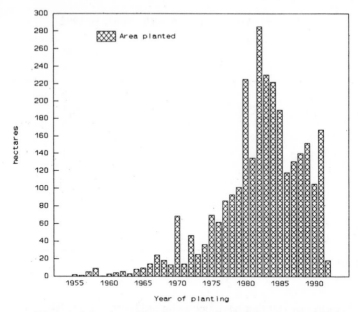

Figure 4.1: Age distribution of rubber area in 1992

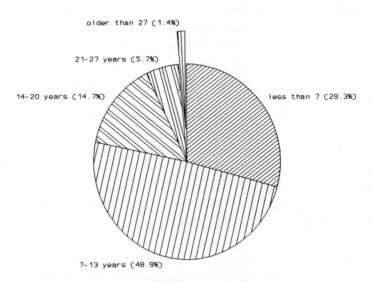

**Figure 4.2: Composition of the total area under rubber
plantation in 1992 by age of the trees**

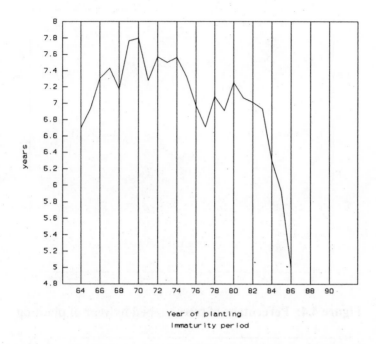

Year of planting
Immaturity period

Figure 4.3: Length of the immaturity period by year of planting

There is not much variation over time, but the period seems to have shortened in the most recently matured plantings. The percentage of trees that come into production after a given number of years is shown in Figure 4.4, while the total number of trees per ha. is presented in Figure 4.5. The percentages tapped start at 2 for area planted in 1986 (i.e. trees that are 6 years old) and increase through 30 for 1985-plantings, 64 for those of 1984 and 79 for those of 1983 to 88 for the plantings of 1982, i.e. 10 year old trees. On an average, a small percentage of trees is not tapped, due to illness, insufficient growth etc. Some years, for which the percentage tapped exceeds 100% have apparent inconsistencies in the data. As shown in Figure 4.5, the average decline per year in number of trees per ha. is about 7 trees per year. This declining number of trees per ha. is partly compensated by a slight rise in the percentages of trees being tapped as the trees grow older.

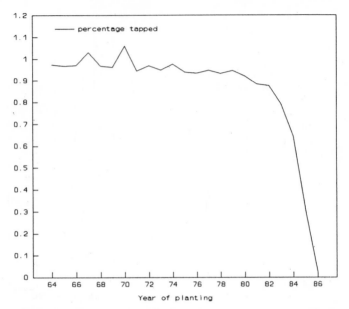

Figure 4.4: Percentage of trees tapped by year of planting

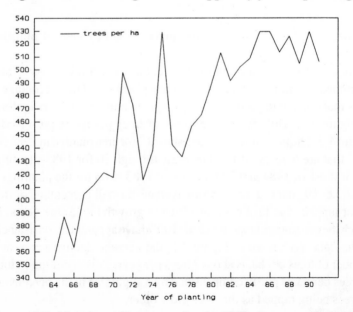

Figure 4.5: Number of trees per ha. in 1992, by year of planting

4.4 Production and labour

Tapping and yield profiles

The rise in the percentages of trees being tapped as the trees grow older can also be seen in the number of tapping days obtained. Figure 4.6 shows the average number of tapping days by year of planting. After an initial steep rise when trees come into production, the number of tapping days per year shows a mildly increasing tendency.

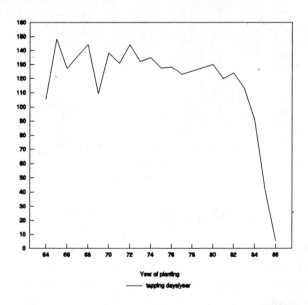

Figure 4.6: Average tapping days by year of planting

The group means by year of planting were also a source for information on the yield profile, i.e. the pattern of yield per hectare as the trees grow older. Figure 4.7 shows the means of the data. On the horizontal axis the years of planting are given. The most common way of presenting a yield profile is by putting th age on the horizontal axis. Such a case would just be the reverse of Figure 4.7.

Labour input

Rubber production requires on average 160 working days per hectare. The bulk of the workload (83%) is spent on tapping, while other

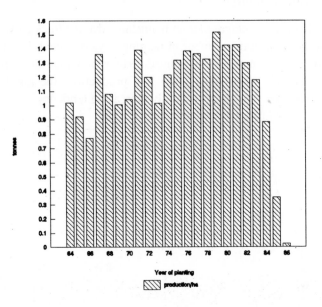

Figure 4.7: Average production per ha.

activities require 17% of the total labour input. Most work is carried out by hired labour (74%). A quarter is done by family members, who tend to be engaged in tapping more than in the other activities. Table 4.6 presents details.

The high share of hired labour in total labour seems to be in line with the fact that 53% of the households do not consider farming as their main occupation (see Table 4.1). A possible relationship between the percentage of work carried out by hired labour and the type of occupation in which the household is engaged is indicated in Table 4.7.

The percentage of hired labour is relatively low in households that indicate coolie work to be their occupation and relatively high in households with members who are working as government servants or are self-employed. The average wage received by hired labour is Rs. 35.82 day. The average price received for rubber is Rs. 22.44 kg.

Table 4.6: Labour input per hectare of rubber

	Labour days			Percentages			Percentages by row		
	tapping	other	total	tapping	other	total	tapping	other	total
Family	35	5	40	22	3	25	26	19	25
Hired	98	22	120	61	14	75	74	81	75
Total	133	27	160	83	17	100	100	100	100

Table 4.7: Occupation and share of hired labour

Occupation	Number of households	Percentage of work carried out by hired labour
Government servant	882	90
Self employed	481	86
Others	600	85
Private company employees	292	80
Farmer	2,332	69
Coolie	340	46

4.5 Discarding and replanting rubber

In the survey rubber producers were asked about their plans with respect to discarding. Figure 4.8 shows the total area to be discarded as planned in 1992. Understandably, only farmers envisaging discarding in the near future have answered this question. In 1993, just over 60 hectares were planned to be discarded. Of the total of 2981 hectares under rubber plantations, of which 1910 hectares were productive, this amounts to 2% of the total rubber growing area and a little over 3% of the productive area. In Figure 4.8 the pattern of which the bars are composed, refers to the year of planting of the rubber trees.

Table 4.8 presents the data corresponding to Figure 4.8, and shows the average age of the trees to be uprooted. It is relatively low, at an average age of 23.9 years, with a minimum of 22.4 years in 1993.

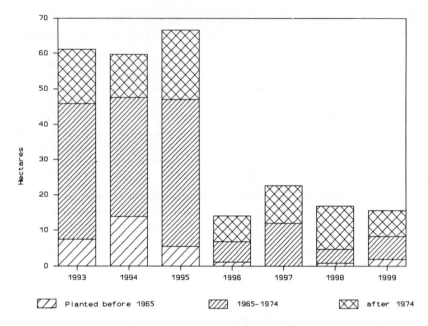

Figure 4.8: Planned discarding

Based upon the figures for expected uprooting in 1993 and composition of the rubber growing area in 1992 the probabilities of tree belonging to specific age-groups being discarded are shown in Table 4.9.

Table 4.8: Area to be discarded and average age of trees
at the time of discarding

	Area (ha)	Age (years)
1993	61	22.4
1994	60	25.4
1995	67	23.9
1996	14	23.3
1997	23	23.6
1998	17	23.2
1999	16	24.9
2000	5	26.8
average		**23.9**

Table 4.9: Planned shares discarded in 1993 by year of planting

year of planting	age	share
1991-1986	0-6 year	0
1985-1981	7-11 year	0
1980-1976	12-16 year	1.72
1975-1971	17-21 year	9.93
1970-1966	22-26 year	15.89
1965-1961	27-31 year	21.46
1960-1951	32-41 year	14.55

Nearly all farmers in the sample intend to replant rubber on the area that is to be discarded. Only in 19 cases (out of 620) rubber cultivation is planned to be discontinued. For both the categories of farmers, i.e. the replanters and those who have decided to plant other crops in the discarded rubber growing area, "economic benefit" was given as by far the main reason for doing so, and "steady income" is for both groups a secondary reason.

In addition to farmers' intentions regarding the use to which they will put plots after discarding, they were also asked what they grew before the present rubber crop, and what other crops could be grown on the plot. Only 21% of the area of those who responded was cultivated with rubber and most area was, therefore, new planted with rubber. The reasons cited as to why these people decided to switch to rubber were "expected economic benefit" from growing rubber in the first place and "other crop not economically viable" as - at some distance - the second. Most farmland was switched from coconut (29.4%) or tapioca (7.8%) to rubber, while another 33% was vacant before, as is shown in Table 4.10. The other crops that can be cultivated in the present rubber growing area are (again) mainly coconut and tapioca and, to a lesser extent, cashew.

Finally, the households were asked what other crops they grew in addition to rubber. This is shown in Table 4.11, which also shows which crops were grown before the existing crops, and which crops are to be cultivated after the present crop. Out of the total area reported in answer to the question on the next crop, only 5.4% is planned to be grown with

Table 4.10: Crops grown earlier in the existing rubber growing area and other crops that could be grown in the rubber growing plot

	crops grown before				competitive crops			
	# of observations	average (ha.)	total (ha.)	%	# of observations	average (ha.)	total (ha.)	%
Rubber	153	0.66	101.0	21.1	2	0.73	1.5	0.3
Cashew	34	0.69	23.5	4.9	11	0.72	7.9	1.7
Paddy	4	0.93	1.6	0.3	0	0	0	0
Cocoa	2	0.59	1.2	0.2	6	0.41	2.5	0.5
Coffee	1	1.80	1.8	0.4	1	0.40	0.4	0.1
Coconut	91	1.55	141.1	29.4	436	0.85	370.6	80.6
Arecanut	6	0.38	2.3	0.5	0	0	0	0
Pepper	8	0.45	3.6	0.8	6	0.52	3.1	0.7
Tapioca	91	0.41	37.3	7.8	127	0.55	69.9	15.2
Plantain	6	0.44	2.6	0.6	3	0.43	1.3	0.3
Ginger	2	0.47	0.9	0.2	1	0.20	0.2	0
Coconut/ Cocoa	1	1.64	1.6	0.3	0	0	0	0
Coconut/ Pepper	1	0.32	0.3	0.1	2	0.61	1.2	0.3
Others	9	0.53	4.8	1.0	1	1.02	1.0	0.2
Vacant	223	0.70	156.1	32.5	0	0	0	0
Total	632		479.6	100	596		459.5	100

rubber. Hence no (further) shift of land of present growers towards rubber can be expected. The reasons for this are given in Table 4.12. Those who have decided not to grow rubber, claim to have either other reasons, or that the area is not suited for rubber cultivation. For them economic benefit is of minor importance. Those rare rubber cultivators who have decided to grow rubber in the plot on which currently other crops, are being grown mention 'economic benefit' as the main reason for doing so.

Table 4.11: Other crops grown, crops grown before the existing crops, and crops that are going to be grown

	present area (ha.)	before area (ha.)	next area (ha.)	present (%)	before (%)	next (%)
Rubber	0	6.4	4.7	0	0	5.4
Cashew	59.8	17.2	2.0	6.4	1.9	2.3
Paddy	227.4	185.7	50.0	24.2	20.7	57.6
Cocoa	8.8	3.7	1.0	0.9	0.4	1.1
Coffee	31.5	0.5	0	3.4	0.1	0
Coconut	420.0	127.5	18.4	44.7	14.2	21.2
Arecanut	25.8	7.6	0.3	2.8	0.8	0.3
Pepper	100.4	4.8	3.5	10.7	0.5	4.0
Tapioca	36.5	37.2	5.5	3.9	4.2	6.4
Others	22.6	14.4	1.0	2.4	1.6	1.2
Plantain	1.0	0.2	0.0	0.1	0	0
Coconut/Cocoa	0.6	0	0	0.1	0	0
Plantain/Tapioca	4.8	4.4	0.4	0.5	0.5	0.5
Vacant	0	486.0	0	0	54.3	0
Total	939.3	895.52	86.78	100	100	100

Table 4.12: Reasons for the decision on growing rubber in plots presently not under rubber

	number of observations	
	no rubber	rubber
Economic benefit	72	38
Uneconomic	9	1
Steady income	0	1
Not suitable for rubber	154	1
Not depending on rubber only	5	1
Others	321	1
Total	561	43

5

MODELLING FARMER BEHAVIOUR
AT THE MICRO-LEVEL

5.1 Introduction

In Chapter 4 the results of the survey among 4000 rubber farmers were summarized in verbal and in statistical terms. In this chapter the answers to the questions in the questionnaire information are used to construct a model of farmer behaviour at the micro-level. We concentrate on yield profiles (section 5.2) and discarding and replanting decisions (sections 5.3 and 5.4). In the following chapter the same will be done at the macro-level relying on features and assumptions on farmers' behaviour as could be derived from the micro-model developed in this chapter.

5.2 Production and labour

Tapping and yield profiles

The percentage of trees being tapped rises as the trees grow older. This is also borne out by the number of tapping days. Figure 5.1 again shows the average number of tapping days by year of planting. Also included here in the figure is an estimated relationship, that is used to express the relationship between the age of the tree and the number of tapping days in mathematical terms. After an initial steep rise when trees come into production, the number of tapping days per year shows a mildly increasing tendency. The estimated relationship for the number of tapping days is

$$\text{days} = -557.6 + 130.0 \text{ Age} - 6.2 \text{ Age}^2 \text{ } if \text{ Age} < 11$$
$$(8.8) \quad (8.4) \quad (6.6)$$
$$\text{days} = 124.4 + 0.83 \text{ Age } if \text{ Age} > 10$$
$$(2.3)$$

where the constant term in the second relationship is estimated so as to provide a smooth transition from one equation to the other at the age of 10. The $R^2 = 0.99$, and the equations were estimated with weighted least squares over the means of the planting years from 1964 until 1986.

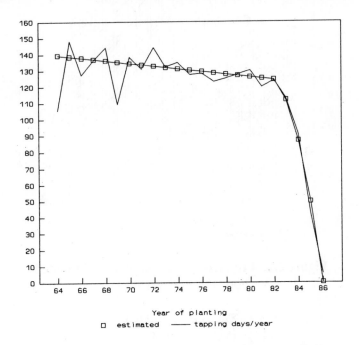

Year of planting

□ estimated   ———— tapping days/year

Figure 5.1: Tapping days by year of planting: means and estimated values

The group means for year of planting were also a source of information on the yield profile, i.e. the pattern of yield per hectare as the trees grow older. Figure 5.2 shows the means of the data and the estimated relationship. Also included in the figure is the "simulated" relationship that uses the estimated rather than the actual number of tapping days as one of the input variables. The relationship was estimated over the same data points. The particular forms chosen, with both age and 1/age as explanatory variables makes it possible that the estimate is a curved relationship that is not necessarily symmetric.

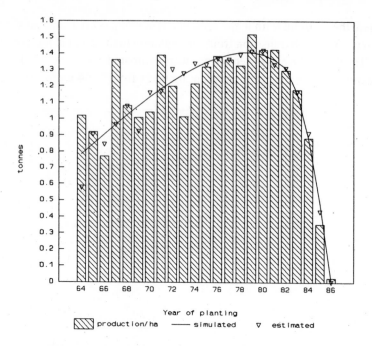

**Figure 5.2: Production per ha.: means, estimated
and 'simulated' values**

production = 2924.5 − 87.6 Age − 14927.6/Age + 6.06 days
$\quad\quad\quad$ (4.5)   (5.6)   (4.4)   (3.9)

As shown, in addition to age, the number of tapping days plays a role,
even though these days by themselves depend on age. According to this
relationship, an increase in tapping days per year by one day would, for
each age class, lead to an additional production of 6 kg. per ha.
Maximum production per ha. is estimated to be obtained at the age of 13.

5.3 Discarding and replanting rubber

As described in Chapter 4 rubber producers were asked about their plans
with respect to discarding. The total area to be discarded as planned in
1992 was shown in Figure 4.8 and in Table 4.8. Based upon the data used
for Table 4.8, a model was estimated to give a mathematical relationship

between age and probability of the discarding. The term 'probability' refers to an individual farmer, who has a certain probability of discarding his plot at some age of the trees. At the aggregate level of the population, these probabilities are equal to the ratios of the discarded area of each age group and the total area of that age. The model assumes that the probabilities can be represented by a logistic function of the form:

$$prob_k = [1 - \exp(-\alpha_2 k)] / [1 + \alpha_1 \exp(-\alpha_2 k)]$$

which, for k=0, takes the value of 0 and for k tending to infinity, tends to unity.

The data in the survey apply to plots that have trees of a certain age in 1992, and are to be discarded in some years time. We need therefore, a version of the discarding function that will represent the probability of certain trees being discarded in year t (with t=0 in 1992), conditional on being i year old in 1992. This probability is given by

$$prob_{t/i} = [1 - \exp(-\alpha_2 t)] / [1 + \alpha_1 \exp\{-\alpha_2 (t + i)\}]$$

This equation has been estimated with the data obtained from the survey. The estimation is done in two ways. One is to use the data to calculate the percentage of total area of age 'i' in 1992, that has been discarded in or before year t, where t=1,...,17 (2010 being the last year for which discarding was announced). As the data are provided by only a small group of farmers it is discontinuous in nature. The first approach is to use these data only. The second approach is to calculate all intermediate years as well and to behave as if in the intermediate years no discarding will take place. The ages of the trees in 1992 range from 8 to 35 years. The formula was estimated using non-linear least squares techniques.

The results of simulation using model 1 are presented below in Figures 5.3 and 5.4. As shown in Figure 5.3, the approximation by one discarding function, describing all age classes is only partially successful, as in particular the planned discarding of the lower age groups is not adequately represented by the estimated line. There appears to be a tendency towards discarding at a later age for trees that are still young in 1992. This, however, may be due to the nature of the answer: it is

Table 5.1: Results of the regression analysis

Results of model 1 (using only reported years):

coefficient	standard error
$\alpha_1 =$ 10912.57	5821.26
$\alpha_2 =$ 0.423	0.0217

data: n = 202

mean time until discarding = 7.0

estimated mean age at the time of discarding

(equal to ln $(\alpha_1)/\alpha_2$): mμ = 21.98 years

Results of model 2 (using calculated data on intermediate years):

coefficient	standard error
$\alpha_1 =$ 12371.25	4631.59
$\alpha_2 =$ 0.414	0.0151

data: n = 476

mean time until discarding = 9

estimated mean age at the time of discarding

(equal to ln $(\alpha_1)/\alpha_2$): mμ = 22.76 years.

---

planned rather than observed discarding, and the actual practice may be that trees are discarded at an earlier age than now envisaged. Note, however, that the data do reveal that discarding is distributed over age classes: it is not confined to some (old) age groups, and it implies that some area of virtually any age class can be found to be discarded in each year.

5.4 Net present values and timing of replanting

The yield profile that was estimated in section 4.4 for the age-wise cross-section of the trees with respect to the year 1992, is used for the calculation of net present values of rubber production. We assume that

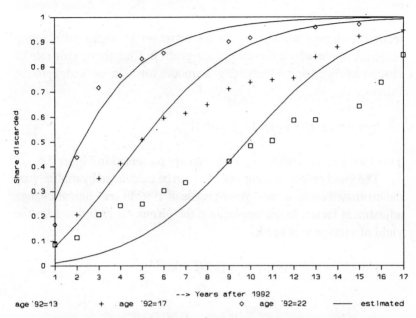

Figure 5.3: Estimated discarding function for 3 1992-age groups; and corresponding data on discarded shares

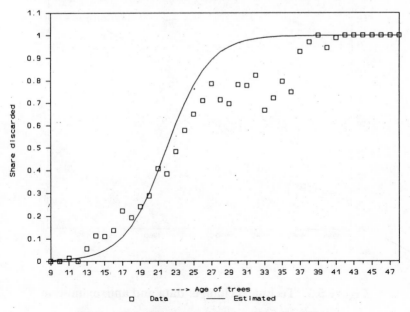

Figure 5.4: Estimated discarding function

technical change is only due to the adoption of improved planting material, about which the details are given in Chapter 6. This rate of change has been approximated by a smooth function, according to the formula:

$$tp_t = 0.2 + 0.8/[1 + \exp\{1972 - t)/8\}]$$

This function, and the underlying data are presented in Figure 5.5.

The yield profile of a vintage can then be calculated by multiplying the estimated cross-section yield-profile of 1992 by a technical-change adjustment factor. In our application the formula is as follows for the yield of vintage s, at age k:

$$yld(s,k) = yldest(k)\{tp(s)/tp(1992 - k)\}^{0.5}$$

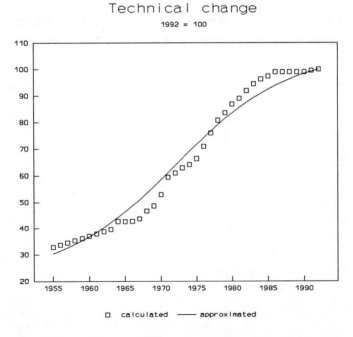

Figure 5.5: Technical change: data and approximation

where yldest(k) is the estimated yield in 1992 of trees k years old, which is then standardized to vintage-1992 level by dividing by the tp-factor for the vintage of these trees, equal to 1992-k, and then adjusted to the vintage s by multiplying by tp(s). Finally, the adjustment factor for technical change has been raised to the power 0.5. This accounts for a mitigation of the effect of technical change on actual yields. The measurement of tp was done at the research station level; in actual applications the effect is assumed to be 50% less. The results are as shown in Figure 5.6.

The next step was to use the estimated number of tapping days, and the resulting yield to calculate the monetary returns per hectare. Yields were multiplied by the average RMA4-prices, deflated by the consumer price index to the level of 1992, and days were multiplied by the

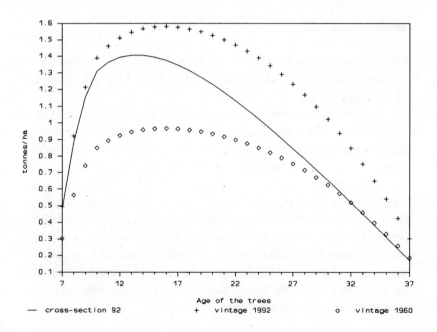

**Figure 5.6: Yield profiles of two vintages,
and cross-section estimate**

assumed wages per days, equal to Rs. 40 at 1992 prices. Gross returns are

yields * price - days * wage.

In addition, we used the replanting subsidies as applicable over the years. Direct costs involved in establishing an hectare of rubber plantation can, in the Indian case, be put at Rs. 40,000 (Rubber Board, 1992), divided over the first seven years after planting, and including clearing, planting, fertilization, spraying, weeding soil conservation etc. The cost of tapping rubber is estimated to be equal to the cost of the tapper, which is put at a rounded figure of Rs. 40 per day (source: survey). For earlier years, these figures for costs and wages have been adjusted by applying the inflation rates.

Replanting subsidies

Over the years there have been various incentives given to the farmers to mitigate the costs involved in replanting. Table 5.2 gives a summary of these incentives.

Replanting behaviour is assumed to be related to the Net Present Value (NPV) of the total income stream, from new planting, which is then compared with the present value of the currently standing rubber trees. As these trees grow older, their productive capacity declines, and it becomes more attractive to consider replanting. Theoretically, this step should be taken when the current income falls below the amount of the interest on the NPV of newplanted trees. To calculate these NPVs we need first to calculate the net income per ha. at each age, and in each year. The aspect of age is important, as yields change with age, and the year is important as prices change from one year to the other, as also because the technology incorporated in the planting material differs over the years. The formula employed is

$$Y(i,t) = y(i,t) * p(t) - w(t) * days(i),$$

where $p(t)$ is the price of rubber in year t; $w(t)$ the daily wage rate in year t; days(i) the number of tapping days for age i and $y(i,t)$ is the yield at

Table 5.2: Cash subsidies for replanting
(Rs/ha., given in 7 instalments)

period 1957-1959
for smallholders (up to 50 acres)   for large growers

	subsidy		subsidy
first 5 acres	988	first 20 acres	741
next 5 acres	927	next 30 acres	680
next 5 acres	865	beyond 50 acres	618
beyond 15 acres	803		

period 1960-1974
all growers: 2471
smallholders (up to 15 acres):
    free planting material
    fertilizer at 50% subsidy

period 1975-1979

smallholders up to 2 ha	7500	large growers	3000
smallholders 2-20 ha	5000		

smallholders (up to 15 acres):
    free planting material
    fertilizer at 50% subsidy

period 1980-1984

smallholders up to 20 ha	5000	large growers	3000

smallholders (up to 6 ha):
   costs of planting material reimbursed
      fertilizer at 50% subsidy
      interest subsidy 3%

period 1985-1992
all growers in non-traditional area   5000
smallholders up to 5 ha in traditional areas   5000
all growers: interest subsidy on loan
        availed from Banks 3%
        assistance for polybagged
        plants up to Rs. 2700/ha

Source: Rubber Board.

age i of trees tapped in year t, i.e. coming from the vintage t-i. Based on this income Y(i,t) and, in the first 7 years, the cost of planting [costs (i,t) (i,t), and the subsidies in these years], we can calculate the Net Present Value (NPV).

$$NPV_1(t,0)= SUM \{ [Y(i,t)\text{-costs}(i,t) + \text{subsidies } (i,t)]/(1+r)^i \};$$
$$\text{summation for } i=0,..,T$$

For each year, the NPV is calculated for one cycle with length T, where T is calculated so as to find the optimal timing of replanting if there were no further technical change, i.e. so that the NPV(t,0), through infinite repetitions, is maximal. The NPV(t,0) for infinite duration, at cycle length T is calculated as

$$NPV_{inf}(t,0) = NPV_1 (t,0)/[1 - 1/(1 + r)^T]$$

To calculate the NPV of a current stand at age i NPV(t,i), we perform the summation over the Y(i,t) starting from i until year T, followed by an infinite series of cycles of length T. The optimal timing of replanting of a present crop is, of course, dependent on the technical changes that have taken place since the trees were planted. The criterion used here in calculating the timing of replanting is that net income from one further year of tapping should no longer exceed the interest on the NPV of a new planting in this year. Figure 5.7 shows the NPVs calculated on the basis of two assumptions on the expected future price.

As shown in Figure 5.7, NPV calculations are highly dependent on the assumed prices. If we assume that the farmer thinks that future prices will the same (in real terms) as the prices in the current year, then the volatile pattern, indicated by squares in Figure 5.7 emerges, but if the assumption is that prices will be Rs. 30/kg in real terms (which was the actual real mean price over the period 1960-1990) then the steadily rising graph emerges. The rise is due to the ever increasing yields per ha, and to some changes in the subsidies and costs that occurred over the years. If, in some year, prices are relatively high, and farmers expect future prices to return to the average value of Rs.30/kg, then it will be attractive to replant in that year only if the yield is very low, that is if the

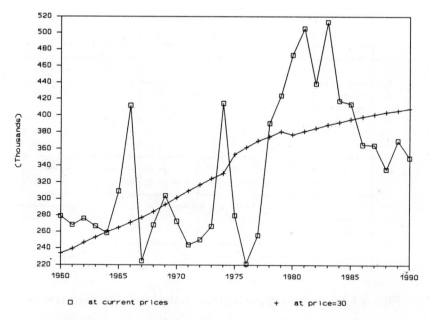

Figure 5.7: Net present values of newplantings (Rs/ha)

trees are rather old. In years with low prices, but the same average expectation for the future, replanting will have become attractive at younger age. This effect of prices on the timing of replanting is shown in Figure 5.8. The Figure shows in two lines, the optimal timing of replanting for two different assumed prices in the future. The steady line is obtained on the basis of the assumption that the price will be what they are in the year concerned, so that in terms of prices, newplanting is not more attractive than continuation of current tapping while the volatile line is obtained on the basis of the assumption that the future price will be Rs. 30/kg. In the years when the price is high, like 1974, replanting will be attractive only when the trees are rather old, in this example 27 years; while in the years when the price is low, like 1976, replanting the present crop by one which would eventually give the yield when the price is 30/kg would be attractive at the early age of 15. The actual price that farmers consider realistic is expected to lie somewhere in between those two extremes.

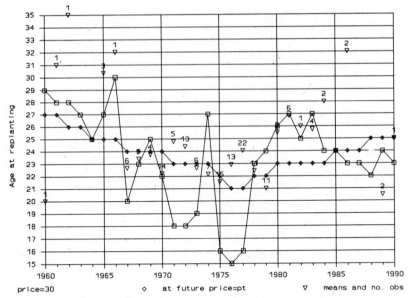

Figure 5.8: Age at replanting: theoretical and observed values

We used the survey data to compute the ages at which replanting had occurred in the past. Only a minority of the farmers in the survey had replanted their present trees, as most of the area was newly planted. Of this minority of some 650 plots, many observations could not be used as either the area or the year of uprooting was not clear. The remaining 160 observations are shown in Figure 5.8. Their mean ages of discarding are shown by triangles and the numbers of observations are added to indicate the extent of reliability of the mean values. The figure suggests that the average age at discarding was higher in the 1960s and the 1980s than in the 1970s. When employing the calculations based on NPVs with the current price as the expected future price, the same pattern emerges. When using a fixed expected price of Rs. 30/kg the resulting pattern shows rather little resemblance with the actual mean values. The impact of current prices on the age of discarding is shown explicitly in Figure 5.9. Theoretical values shown here are those based on the expected price of Rs. 30/kg, which would predict stronger changes in the age of discarding than what actually took place. Yet, some impact is visible: at high prices less discarding appears to take place.

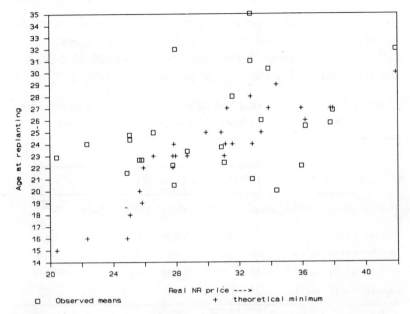

Figure 5.9: Age at replanting as function of current real prices

Another comparison between theoretical and actual values is made by looking at the shares discarded, instead of the average age at discarding. Figure 5.10 presents the relevant information. The shares discarded have been calculated by first reconstructing the past total areas of each age, and then to calculate the ratios of discarded and total areas in each year and age. In Table 5.3 and Figure 5.10, these data have been grouped into four age groups and four time periods. The higher discarding rates of older age groups is clearly visible in all periods, except the first half of the seventies.

To explain changes in discarding rates with time and age, theory would suggest a comparison between - on the one hand - the Net Present Value of continuing tapping, followed by replanting at the optimal time, which is when the interest over the NPV of new planting exceeds income from tapping for one year, and - on the other hand - the NPV of new planting immediately. The calculation of the income streams after newplanting have been based on Rs. 30/kg as the expected price, but the income stream in the near future is evaluated based on the current price

levels. The relationship between this difference in NPV-values and the
shares discarded is shown in Figure 5.11 in which, the letters a, b, c, d
indicate the age group (a=15-19 years old, b=20-24, c=25-29, d=30-34),
and the numbers 1-4 indicate the period (1=1965-69, 2=1970-74,

**Table 5.3: Shares discarded, and differences of NPV of present stand
and NPV and new plantings; grouped by age and years**

Years	15-19		20-24		25-29		30-34	
	shares	dNPVi	shares	dNPVi	shares	dNPVi	shares	dNPVi
1964-96	0.0219	42852.4	0.113	16134.6	0.1670	1101.6	0.25	- 9108.5
1970-74	0.0527	19533.1	0.160	3865.4	0.1531	-3437.8	0.10	- 8944.9
1975-79	0.1469	17268.3	0.188	109.9	0.2839	-6063.2	0.46	- 14273.0
1980-84	0.0092	94197.8	0.027	27384.8	0.3262	1490.8	NA	NA

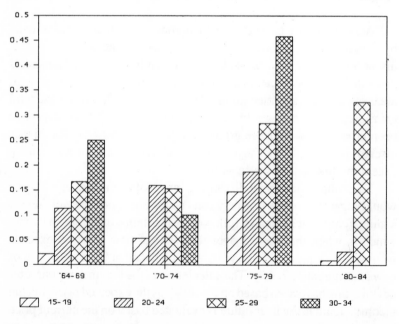

Figure 5.10: Shares discarded by age group and year of uprooting

3=1975-79, 4=1980-84). The changes in discarding shares in the young age group a (15-19 years) seem clearly related to the difference in NPVs, and the same way hold for group b, (20-24 years). For the two older groups, the evidence is less clear.

The logistic relationship, that was estimated is

$$\log [s_{it}/(1 - s_{it})] = -1.54 - 0.03952 \, dNPV_{it}$$
$$(8.9) \quad (6.7)$$

$$R^2 = 0.77$$

where s_{it} is the average share discarded for all age and year combinations in the particular age and time group; $dNPV_{it}$ is the average value (taken in the same way) of the difference between the NPV of the current stand

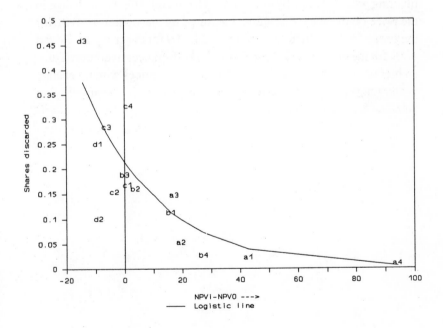

Figure 5.11: Shares discarded as function of difference in NPV values

for at least one year (at current prices), and the NPV of newplanting at the fixed price of Rs. 30/kg.

The two approaches, one on the basis of optimal timing of replanting, and the other based on the explanation of shares discarded, suggest the validity of the NPV concept as indicative of replanting decisions. Although the database for the evidence is meagre, the grouped observations suggest that, (a) at high prices, less discarding takes place and, (b) at times of rapid technical change, more discarding occurs. The effect of prices can be measured by estimating the impact on $dNPV_{it}$ of a change in price. Measured as an elasticity, this effect ranges from 0.58 for the youngest age group to 0.04 for the oldest group, i.e. when changing the current price (and not the expected future, price) by 10%, the average NPV in the group 15-19 years changes by 5.5% in the same direction. The implication is that the difference between the NPV of the current stand and the NPV of new planting would change by even more. The overall effect of a change in the price on the share discarded, measured by elasticities, is -0.82 for the group 15-19, -.36 for the group 20-24, -.09 for the group 25-29 and -0.04 for the oldest group, with no marked differences over time. Thus, an increase of 10% in current (and near-future) prices with no change in the long-term price, induces a decrease in shares discarded lying between 8.2% and 0.4%.

6

NATURAL RUBBER PLANTING AND PRODUCTION POTENTIAL

6.1 Introduction

In this chapter we assess the past potential for natural rubber production in India in relation to plantings and quality of the trees. We investigate the age distribution of the trees, the distribution of planting material and its effect on yield, the past performance of the production of rubber. For this we delve deep into history; such historical information as we could gather will be presented briefly for the reader. Further information is available upon request. This investigation provides us material to design a framework for projections of the future potential production. Both targets and alternative policies for planting are applied for possible future projections. These results are presented in chapter 10.

The general approach (see Section 6.2) is to derive the age distribution of the rubber trees for the years 1955-1991, combine estimates and statistics to derive the yield potential of the trees according to age and planting material, and calculate the 'normal production'. With assumptions on future new planting and the rate of replanting, the potential production for the future is calculated. This is presented in Chapter 10. In section 6.3 we review the evidence on age distribution. Sources available are data on past planting, area data, some recent survey data and publications of the Rubber Research Institute of India (RRII) on the subject. Section 6.4 is devoted to the issue of yield. The standard yield profile is introduced and compared with data on yields of various clones. We distinguish three important types (TJIR11, RRIM600 and RRII105) and show the effects of this planting material on India's NR production. In section 6.5 the procedures for establishing the basis for projections is discussed. We combine the data on area, age distribution and yield potential and compare this with the data on production in the past 25 years. From this information, we derive an estimate for the rate of technical progress, incorporated in the planting material since 1902. In section 6.6 we discuss the classification between the traditional and the non-traditional areas.

6.2 A general framework for natural rubber supply

For perennial crops supply is largely determined by investment decisions in the past while actual supply may be interpreted rather as a decision on the utilization of capacity. Such capacity is often estimated in industry as the maximum possible production, where the normal level of capacity utilization may be around 75%. In our approach we rather prefer to start from such a "normal" level of capacity utilization in view of an optimal long-term rate of exploitation of trees. Such a level of production will be called "normal production".

"Normal production" is defined as the level of production in a certain year, which would have been realized without taking into account the price influence. To assess real developments in the market, only the short-term price effects need to be superimposed. If prices are low, actual production will be below normal production. This could be explained as a proportional reduction in production for the whole area. However, another way to look at it is that less productive area will not be ("fully") exploited. If prices are high, even those areas which are not profitable at average price levels will come back into production. In this section, we describe how normal production can be estimated in relation to other variables.

A hypothetical hectare of rubber trees planted in 1955 provides rubber starting from the 1960s onwards and declining in the 1970s. When the age of the tree is between 20 and 40, a decision about replanting or uprooting must be made because, otherwise, production from that hypothetical area of trees will decline to very low levels in the following years (the yield profile). If this hectare is uprooted (not replanted with NR), the reduction of NR production potential depends on the yield profile and the age of the trees on that hectare at the time of uprooting. If the hectare is replanted with NR, this implies no NR production during the immaturity period. After the immaturity period production starts, following a yield profile. However, the yield profile to be followed will be considerably higher than the old one because of technical progress. Finally, the intensity at which tapping is carried out depends on prices and labour availability. Hence, in analyzing production of natural rubber information on the following factors are essential: planted area, new planting, replanting, uprooting for replanting with other crops or for other purposes, the age of the trees in the area and the yield profiles, technical progress, and other factors influencing normal production and prices.

Estimation of normal production therefore requires answers to the following questions:

a) what is the composition of the total area for NR according to the year of planting (the **vintages**);

b) what are the percentages of trees being uprooted or replanted because of age, disease or damage respectively (the **discarding system**);

c) what is the average yield profile for a hectare of rubber during its life (the **yield profile**);

d) how does **technical progress** in quality of clones affect yield profiles of hectares planted in various years;

e) what is the influence of other exogenous factors on normal production, e.g. weather and slaughter tapping.

Data to do such an analysis are not available as will be clear to anybody familiar with NR statistics. Below, the methodology to incorporate all relevant variables in the analysis is described and it is shown how to create an adequate data base. For further details see Smit (1984).

Area distribution by vintages and discarding systems

An essential element in analyzing NR production is the division of area by age groups, the so-called vintages. A vintage of year s is the area planted in year s e.g. s = 1955. As the years pass by, the 1955 vintage will reduce in size due to uprooting or replanting. Data on area planted per year are reasonably accurate for many years. Other available data include total acreage under rubber plantations and area discarded, both on an annual basis.

A problem arises in determining area distribution by vintages, i.e. the number of hectares planted in year s and still existing in the year of tapping, year t, which is the year of analysis. Discarding of area, meaning uprooting for other crops or replanting by rubber, can be derived for total area, but cannot be classified according to vintages. In other words, it is not known how much of the 1955 vintage is discarded in 1956, 1957 and so on. However, little discarding is assumed in the first few years; then, when the tree becomes less productive, discarding increases.

If the distribution of the area by vintage could be known in a certain year t-1, e.g. 1959, thus giving us a breakdown in terms of area planted 1 year ago, 2 years ago and so on, and if one could know the discarding percentages p_1, p_2, for age 1, 2 etc., then it would be easy to calculate how much would be left for each vintage in year 1960. Using the same percentages one could then carry on and calculate the area distribution for 1961, 1962, etc. One does not know the p_k exactly: it is assumed that p_k approximately follows a sigmoid curve (cf. Chapter 4). By summing up all discarded area over the vintages in 1960, one obtains total discarded area in 1960 and similarly for the later years. The p_k must be chosen in such a way that the calculated discarded area in each year equals the actual discarded area in the same year. This implies for each year a specific average age, or point of infection, shifting the sigmoid curve to the left when there was a lot of replanting and uprooting, and shifting it to the right if discarding was more limited.

Yield profiles and technical progress

From the first year of tapping onwards all NR clones follow a particular pattern in yield over time, which resembles a skewed bell-shaped curve, increasing steeply first and, later-on, declining slowly. Because of the large degree of aggregation that is inevitable in the set-up of this study, an average of the various yield profiles has been used. The actual yield profile is lower than the standard yield profile. The standard yield profile therefore needs to be multiplied with a certain factor, in order to reduce the standard yield profile to actual levels. This multiplication factor is different for different countries, and, within countries, for estates and smallholdings, possibly as a result of the selection of clones. This selection of clones of which a certain vintage is composed is fixed once a vintage is in the ground. However, the composition of different vintages and therefore different planting years) may vary over time, implying that the multiplication factor may need to increase over time in view of embodied technical progress. Each vintage is assumed to have an average yield profile, which is a constant fraction of the standard yield profile: if for example a yield profile is estimated to be 0.3 times the standard yield profile, then the profile is suppressed to 30% of the original shape. Of course, later vintages may be composed of better clones, thus increasing average yield. In the example, the fraction of 0.3 may become 0.4 for the vintage planted a number of years later. The fractions are estimated per vintage by relating area and standard yield profile to production and then deriving the fractions which create actual yield profiles that are consistent with area composition and production.

Specification of a normal-production function

We are now in a position to calculate normal production by combining vintages, discarding systems, yield profiles and technical progress. Of course data on normal production are not available. The normal production function may be specified mathematically as

$$q_{n,t} = \sum_s y_{t-s} a_{ts}$$

$$y_{t-s} = f(s)\bar{y}_{t-s}$$

with $q_{n,t}$ = normal production of NR

s = year of planting

t = year of tapping

$f(s)$ = embodied technical progress function

$\bar{y}_{t-s}$ = yield according to the standard yield profile, age = t-s

y_{t-s} = yield profile adjusted for technical progress

a_{ts} = area of vintage s still remaining in year t

The standard yield profile, the development of the standard yield over time, is adjusted for the length of the immaturity period, which may vary around 6 years. There are many possible specifications for f(s) of which linear functions are easiest to apply.

6.3 Planting patterns and age distribution

In order to derive the age distribution of trees in any year, data are required not only on newplanting but also on replanting and discarding. Time series on newplanting, replanting and discarding are not available. Especially for the period up to 1955-56 there is little information available [see Indian Rubber Statistics (several issues up to 1952) published by the Ministry of Agriculture, Government of India]. 'A short note on rubber plantation industry in India' (1947) published by the Indian Rubber Board and the 'Report of the Plantation Enquiry Commission (1956) published by the Government of India give data on newplanting, replanting and total area for certain selected periods up to 1955. Some inconsistencies are noticed in the figure given in these publications. Indian Rubber Statistics (IRS) published by the Rubber Board beginning from 1958 gives annual figures of newplanting, replanting and total area. The figures given in the earlier issues of IRS were compiled from the registration records. Under the Rubber Act all rubber growers have to register their area in the books of the Rubber Board. Till 1962 registration of rubber was carried out by the Board solely on the strength of information furnished by the rubber growers. From 1963 onwards registration is carried out after field inspection and appropriate correction of data reported by the rubber growers. During the 1970s and 1980s sample studies were carried out by the Board periodically to estimate the area under tapping, total area, production etc. Such studies have revealed discrepancies and to some extent registration statistics were adjusted with the help of such surveys. Since 1978 there was a spurt in planting activities due to the improvement in rubber prices and introduction of cash subsidy for newplanting. As a result, the number of rubber growing units has increased tremendously causing practical difficulties in carrying out registration systematically.

The number of rubber growing units is estimated to have increased from 220 thousand in 1980-81 to over 800 thousand in 1991-92. To improve the area statistics and collection of additional particulars, a census of rubber area was initiated in 1988-89. Enumeration of about 24% of the rubber growing villages was conducted during 1988-89, 16% during 1990-91 and 23% during 1992-93. By 1994-95 the first round will be completed. The census reports are being processed.

For the present study, the main source for area figures are the statistics reported in the IRS from 1955-56 onwards. An analysis of the data given in the various publications cited above reveals that the area under rubber plantations has increased over the years as follows:

1902	-	200 ha.	1970-71	-217,000 ha.
1925	-	31,000 ha.	1980-81	-284,000 ha.
1950	-	75,000 ha.	1990-91	-475,000 ha.
1960-61	-	144,000 ha.	1991-92	-488,500 ha. (provisional).

We take 1955-56 (henceforth referred to as 1955) as the starting year for the vintage matrix. A vintage matrix contains information on area under rubber plantations in all years, according to the 'vintage' (the year of planting). If the age distribution of 1955 is known, those of later years can be derived with the help of data on new planting, replanting (the sum of these two constitutes the area of age zero in the next year), discarded area and a device to distribute total discarded area over age classes. This device is the discarding function. Figure 6.1 shows the shape of the discarding function for an average age at the time of discarding (the so-called mu (μ), see Appendix A) which is close to 30. After adjusting for total area, this function yields, for each age group, the percentage of last year's area that will be discarded.

Before deriving the age distribution in the years after 1955, the distribution in the base year 1955 must be established. How this is done is presented in detail in Appendix B. Total planting in 1954 was 4,746 ha., and in 1955 no less than 10,061 ha. was planted. The age distribution over the other age groups, derived with this procedure, is presented in Figure 6.2.

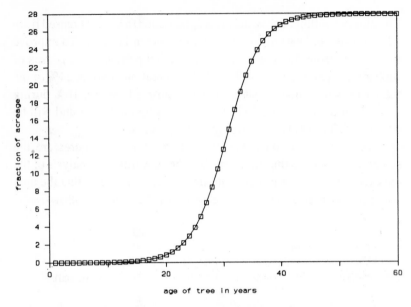

Figure 6.1: The discarding function

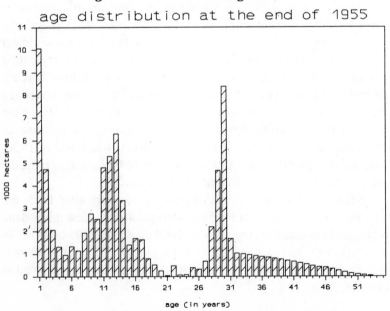

Figure 6.2: Age distribution at the end of 1955-56

Data provided by the Rubber Board form the basis for the subsequent derivation of age distributions for 1956-1991. If discarding is assumed to follow this particular pattern over time as formalised in the discarding function, the parameter μ of this function (representing the average age at the time of discarding if the age distribution is homogeneous) needs to be adjusted to fit the data on discarded area. This leads to a decline in the μ from 40 in 1955 to 27 in the mid-sixties, after which it rises slowly to 32.8 in 1991 (see Figure 6.3). This indicates that trees in the fifties and sixties were discarded at an earlier age than more recently. The cause lies in the high rate of planting of 1926, which trees are not fully discarded until 1966. Given the level of discarding, the *mu* must be rather high if a peak like that of 1926 is included in estimating the discarding. Once this disappears, younger age groups must take increasing shares of total discarding, thus reducing the average age at the time of discarding. The resulting age distribution is shown in Figure 6.4. The lowest part, 0-6 years old, reaches a high level in the late 1980s because of massive planting since 1978. The age distribution implied by this

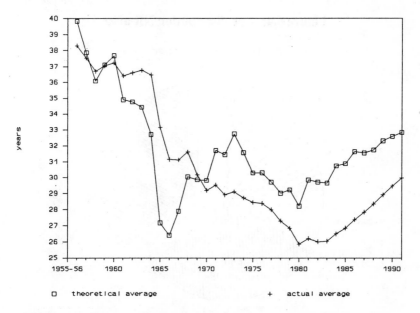

Figure 6.3: Theoretical and actual mean age of the trees at the time of discarding

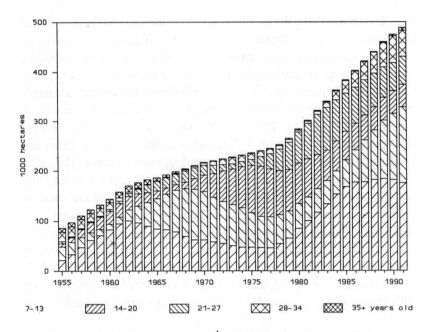

Figure 6.4: Age distribution NR area

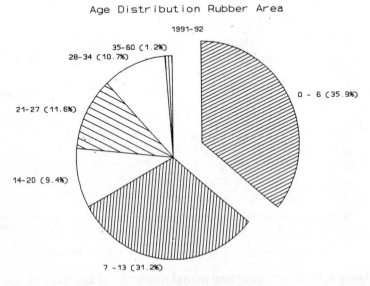

Figure 6.5: Age distribution 1991-92

model at the end of 1991-92 is given in Figure 6.5. Here, 37% of the area is under 7 years old. Tappable area is more than the balancing 63% however, because many trees of the RRII-105 series can be tapped earlier. According to the model 71% should be tappable in 1992 which is confirmed by census data showing that by 1992-93 70% was being tapped.

6.4 Yield and technical progress

Once the age distribution is known, production can be calculated easily. The area of each age group has to be multiplied with the corresponding yield. Between the ages of 5 to 9 years, the trees are opened for tapping. (For a survey of age at opening see Krishnan Kutty, George Jacob and Haridasan, 1982). They show that average age at opening for formerly popular varieties like GG1 and GG2 is 5-1/2, whereas TJIR1 material is tapped for the first time in the 7th year, and RRIM600 on average in the 8th year.

From the first year of tapping onwards, yield per hectare is determined by the type of material, the intensity of tapping and the density of the trees. Starting with the latter, recommended density is normally some 450 trees/ha. This can be less, when interplanting or intercropping is done, as is the case with many smallholdings (see Unny and Jacob) 1972 or Ramakrishna Pillai, 1974). Density can be more when small farmers try to maximize revenues per ha. from their plot: Toms Joseph *et al.* (1989) report a density of 536 trees/ha. (average over various varieties) in 1986. Over time, density of trees diminishes due to storm damage, diseases etc. until it reaches about 250 at old age. Haridasan (undated) reports the figure of 250 trees/ha. for smallholdings in the replanting scheme of the late 60s-early 70s. Haridasan and Srinivasan (1985) give a figure of 227 trees/ha. at the time of felling, and say that this figure stood at 184 in an earlier survey of 1972-73. Recent census data show that average planting density of immature area stood at 545 trees/ha., and of mature area at 446 trees/ha.; thereafter the density declines to an average of 290 trees/ha. for the age group of over 35 years old.

Tapping intensity in India is fairly high. Standard practice on estates is to follow an S2D2 system which implies tapping on every alternate day, excluding rainy days and the wintering period. The number of

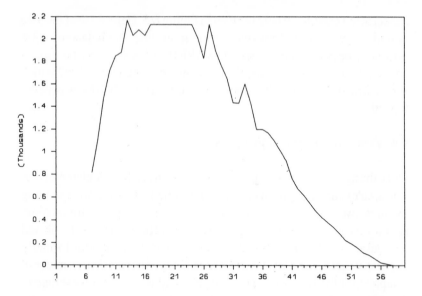

Figure 6.6: Standard yield by year of tapping in kg/ha.
Source: Smit (1984)

tapping days reported by the Rubber Research Institute of India amount to 180 days per year on an S2D1 system, in an S2D2 system, 135 days with rainguarding and 103 days without rainguarding. In S2D3 system there are 90 tapping days per year. Many smallholders appear to tap more often. Unny and Jacob (1972) report on the basis of a survey done in 1969-70 that 53% of the farmers follow the S2D1 and 42% the S2D2 systems respectively. The recent census data show that in 1990-91 the percentage of farmers following the S2D1 system has gone down to 28%, and the S2D2 system was practised by 65% of the farmers. In terms of yield per ha., the influence of tapping intensity in Unny and Jacob's survey was that the S2D1 system yielded more than the S2D2 system, the difference lying between 15% (for unselected seedlings) and 29% (for budded stumps). For the derivation of 'normal' production levels, we assume tapping intensity to follow a constant pattern over time. In the analysis of short term price responsiveness of farmers we assume that changes in tapping intensity constitute the supply response.

Similar to the approaches followed for Malaysian smallholdings, Indonesia and Thailand (see Burger and Smit, 1989), we start from a standard yield profile in terms of production per ha. in which constant tapping pattern is assumed, along with good tapping practice,and normal decline of density. In Figure 6.6 this standard yield is plotted.

If we would apply this yield profile to all the years for which we have the age distribution, and calibrate the results to the average amount produced in the period, then we end up with an estimate that is too low in the earlier part and too high in the later part of the period. Actually, the ratio between high (in 1989) and low (in 1955) is about 2.

Technical progress in the planting material was the main cause of the increase in yield. While in the earlier period progress was made by using more buddings instead of seedlings, after 1963 new varieties were introduced with intrinsically higher yield. Figure 6.7 is derived from IRS statistics and gives a survey of the types of material distributed by the Rubber Board and/or by licensed traders. This covered about 80% of the area planted during 1968-85. A quick change over from one variety to the other is also noticed. Under the heading "TJIR1 etc.", we have included indigenous polyclonal seedlings and PB1G/GG1 and GG2 seedlings. Distributed seeds and budwood were not included in the calculation. Census data show that by 1970-71 72.7% of tapped area was under budgrafted material, compared to only 15.4% in 1969-70.

The extent to which these new varieties contribute to production depends on the yield profiles. Data on yield per variety are difficult to collect, as smallholders often grow a mixture of varieties and hardly keep record of production. Table 1 in Appendix C shows therefore mainly data from the estates. To judge the performance of the varieties, we compared the figures with the standard yield profile of Figure 6.6, and checked whether we can assume that the profile was similar, i.e. differed only in proportion, but not in shape. Details are given in Appendix C. We draw the conclusion that as yet no strong evidence exists for changing the yield profile, with the exception of the early years of tapping. This is incorporated in the model by allowing for a one-year shorter immaturity period for the RRII-105 clone. Further evidence for this decrease in length of immaturity period was provided in Chapter 4, Figure 4.3.

The data underlying the tables and figures are taken from fields that were actually tapped. In our vintage approach we need a link between age and yield, and therefore a link between age and year of tapping and

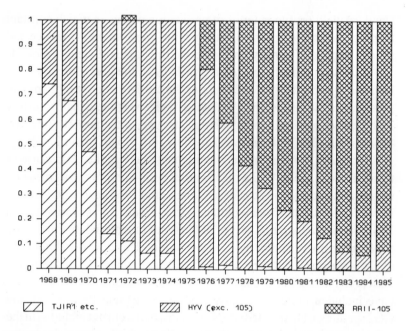

Figure 6.7: Shares of planting material in total controlled distribution
Source: IRS 18, Table 42

between year of tapping and yield. The assumption for all years is that a quarter of the trees are opened at the age of five, a quarter at the age of six, a quarter at the age of seven, and a quarter at the age of eight. But with the introduction of RRII-105 between 1975 and 1980, these ages are reduced by one year. This assumption caters for the yield in early years of tapping.`Although in practice, the yields in early years are higher than assumed, this is compensated by our assumption that trees are tapped at an earlier age.

Although data are available at a maximum for the first 15 years of tapping, there are trees that are even older. After consultation with the Rubber Research Institute of India the standard yield for trees older than 20 years has been adjusted with a factor $\exp\{-(t-20)/30\}$. This appeared to be a better assumption in the Indian context. The estimated yield profile for the vintage of 1992, as derived in Chapter 4, is to a high degree proportional to this standard yield profile. Standard yield, now including the averaging due to differential opening and the adjustment, then becomes as shown in Figure 6.8.

As mentioned earlier, applying this profile to all years would lead to a downward bias in the resulting production estimates, as technical progress is not yet included. To assess the degree of technical progress, we used the shares of Figure 6.7, combined with the average values for the relative yield levels from Table 2 in Appendix C. Assuming average relative yield levels of 55% for TJIR1 and other seedlings, 75% for RRIM600 and comparable clones, and 95% for RRII-105, the shares of Figure 6.7 give rise to the technical progress levels as given in Figure 6.9. No change has been assumed after 1985.

6.5 Actual and normal production levels

In the previous sections we reviewed the data available on area, age distribution, yield per hectare of various clones and their shares. Still, this is not enough as a basis for calculating normal production levels. We need all these data for the whole of the period, which implies that we need information on the potential of trees that were in production in 1955, and those that may have been planted in 1956. In addition, the actual adoption of newer clones must be included in the calculations. The data are not exhaustive either and we still have degrees of freedom left. There is lack of data on the actual adoption of new varieties by all replanting and new planting farmers in a year, for example. Do the figures underlying Figure 6.9 cover all planting? There are no data available yet on the type and yield of clones adopted before 1963 and after 1986. And no direct observations are recorded on actual yield by clone on representative small holdings. To bring some light into this matter, assumptions were made and tested on the data that have been collected thus far. The data on area were used to establish the age distribution. Figure 6.7 gave a first idea about technical progress and the data of Table 2 in Appendix C about relative yield. These were combined by additional assumptions for the period before 1963. The area of each age group in each year was then multiplied by the average adjusted standard yield (see Figure 6.8), and by the technical progress factor applicable to the year of planting. For example the area, aged 10

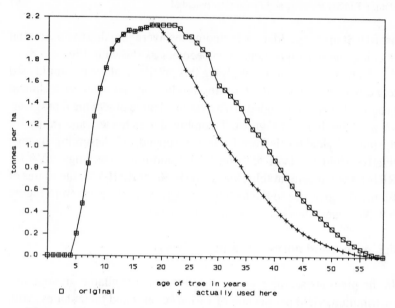

Figure 6.8: Average standard yield, original and adjusted
Note: For RRII-105 clones, ages are reduced by 1, i.e. yield at age 4 is
204 kg/ha. etc.

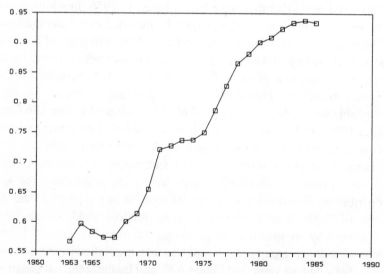

**Figure 6.9: Relative yield, weighted by share of TJIR1,
RRIM600 and RRII-105**
Note: TJIR1=0.55; RRIM600=0.75; RRII-105=0.95.

years in 1965 is multiplied by 1729 (average standard yield of 10 year old trees) and by 0.37 (if this is the technical progress factor for 1965). The resulting total production of 1965 is recorded. This is done for the whole period from 1955 to 1989. The average estimated production (1965-1989) is compared with average actual production in this period. Each year is adjusted so as to make the two averages equal. These final results are compared with actual levels. If any trend remains visible in the ratios of actual to normal production, the technical progress factors are adjusted. These were made so as to arrive at estimates of production, that showed high correlation with the actual figures on production.

For the particular period 1963-1985 it proved desirable to assume that the rate of change was higher than that implied by the data of Figure 6.9. This is probably due to the greater adoption of RRII-105 by smallholders, compared to their earlier adoption of RRIM600 or comparable clones. We estimated that a factor of 0.89 should be applied to the figures of 1963, annually increasing by 0.05 to reach 1 in 1985. For the period from 1955 to 1963 we estimated a gradual increase in the potential yield of planted material as shown in Figure 6.10. Actual average yields around 1960 were the same as in the 1930s and we assumed, therefore, no increase in yield potential before 1955. But yield in the early 1950s were lower than before the war. To accommodate for this, the assumption is introduced that technical progress factor actually declined from 1938 to reach their lowest level in 1947. With these assumptions a reasonable fit of predicted to actual data on production was reached.

Figures 6.11 and 6.12 show the simulated and actual production levels, and their ratios for the period 1965-1989. The overall calibration factor for the period amounted to 0.86, so that the final interpretation of the relative yield levels should be reduced. For example the yield of RRII-105, compared to the standard yield (which was found to be about 0.95) in actual and aggregate practice turns out to be 0.817.

The assumptions on technical progress have been made in such a way that no trend remains in the ratios of actual to normal production, as can be seen in Figure 6.12. Larger deviations from unity are in 1976 (1.07) and 1978 (0.91). A series of low values is found for the period 1965-1970. During the period 1966-74, frequent strikes of tappers affected the production significantly. The Government of India had

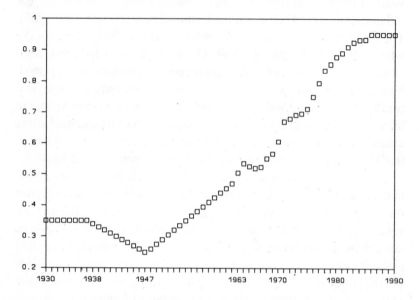

Figure 6.10: Technical progress factors

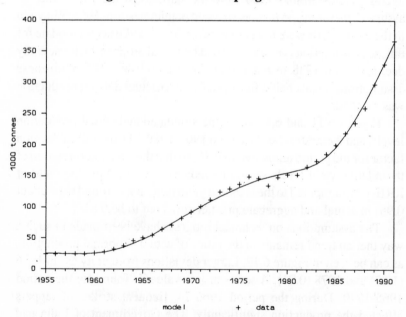

model   +   data

Figure 6.11: Actual and simulated production

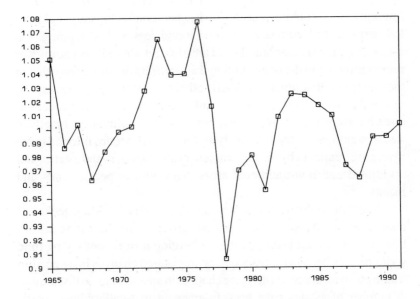

Figure 6.12: Actual over simulated production

declared emergency during June 1975 and it continued up to March 1977. The peaceful conditions helped to harvest a good crop during 1975 and 1976. Again the industry wide strike of tappers during the peak yielding season and adverse climatic conditions significantly reduced the crop in 1978. Labour unrest also affected production during 1979. Nevertheless, the model as it is, is very well capable of simulating the tendencies in the production over time.

6.6 Non-traditional areas

The analysis of the previous sections was based on aggregate data on natural rubber production. Data were aggregated over estates and smallholdings, and over traditional and non-traditional areas.

Data available show that the age distribution in the estate sector is quite homogeneous, whereas the distribution in the non-traditional sector is skewed towards more recent years. This is a good reason to distinguish these two groups from the major group of smallholdings in the traditional area. Other reasons to distinguish these groups are the diverging cultivation practices and in the differences in yield. Yield is lower in the non-traditional area, with less favourable climatic conditions, less experienced cultivation practices and less skilled tapping. On estates, tapping standards and yield are high. Smallholder economics of rubber growing in the non-traditional area differs therefore from that in the traditional area which may lead to other norms for tapping intensities, or tree densities. The estate sector with relatively high and fixed labour costs has its own economic assessment of rubber cultivation. Finally, a strong argument for separate analyses for the three groups is found in the diverging treatment by the government of smallholders and estates, and traditional and non-traditional areas, both with respect to ends and means.

To do the analysis, data on area, age distribution, yield and technical change are required for the separate groups. For the estate sector, however, it has not been possible to develop a sufficiently long time series on area because of inadequately registered changes in ownership leading to inaccuracies in deriving changes in area and thus in discarding. A number of estates have been fragmented to smallholdings, particularly in the 1970s. Therefore the only accurate split-up possible here is the disaggregation between the traditional and the non-traditional areas.

In the non-traditional area, meaning area outside Kerala and Tamil Nadu, only limited production was available before 1955-56. The same age distribution for 1955-56 has been applied as for the whole of India (see Section 6.3). A similar procedure is followed as well to derive the age distribution in the non-traditional area, for the year after 1955. The resulting age distribution in 1989 is given in Figure 6.13. Replanting data for the years before 1981 are not available and are therefore based on assumptions.

Section 6.4 contains a detailed review of the procedure to establish the levels of normal production, adjusted for technical change and calibrated for the years 1965-1990, on the basis of the above derived area and age distributions. The procedure described in the main report was successively applied to the vintage-matrices of the non-traditional area. In the process of calibrating the results so as to fit with the data on production, the levels of production and the technical change were derived. Figure 6.14 shows the data on production and the model trend simulations.

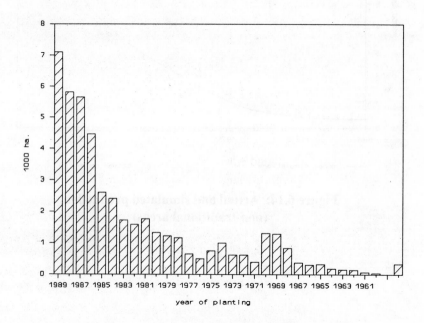

**Figure 6.13: Estimated age distribution in 1989
(non-traditional areas)**

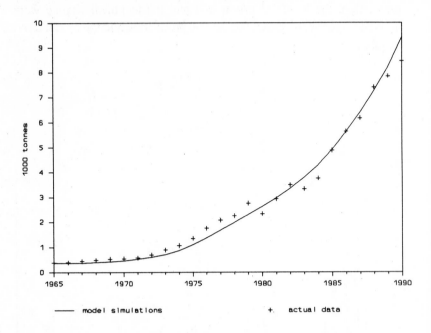

**Figure 6.14: Actual and simulated production
(non-traditional areas)**

Part III
Analysis of Rubber Demand

7

RUBBER DEMAND, GENERAL

7.1 Introduction

In this part the demand side of the Indian rubber market is analyzed. The purpose of this part is to obtain an insight into the empirical developments of the demand side of the rubber market. All data are supplied by the Rubber Board of India. Modelling requires deep knowledge of developments in the past in order to draw lines for the future. Part of that historical information has been included in the text for the reader to better understand and appreciate the modelling decisions made. No attention has yet been paid to the analysis of the export side as this is highly uncertain. For the future some assumptions will be used.

In order to get a picture of demand a short description of the demand side is presented first. Then the causal relationships are elaborated. On the basis of these relationships a model is developed. Finally, the estimation results of the suggested model are reported. The organisation of this part follows the same lines. The description of the demand side is presented in the following section. In Section 7.3. the relationships on the demand side are set out verbally. In Chapter 8 a formal presentation of the model is given and the empirical results are presented.

7.2 An overview of rubber demand by type and end-product

Demand for rubber is made up of consumption, exports and changes in stocks of rubber. Before the Second World War, natural rubber produced in India was almost entirely exported although a small rubber goods manufacturing industry had been in existence in the country since 1920. The first rubber factory, the Bengal Waterproof Ltd., was set up in Calcutta by that time. After the conquest of Malaya (West Malaysia), the East Indies (Indonesia) and other South East Asian countries by Japan during the early years of the war, the position and prospect of the

industry were transformed drastically. The war efforts encouraged the
infant Indian rubber goods manufacturing industry to produce more
rubber goods. The launching of the Five-Year Plans found the country
importing more and more rubber to meet the internal demand. By the
end of the war, there arose a number of factories. By the early fifties,
important factories had set up their purchase offices in Kottayam, the
most notable rubber market in India. In the early 1950s, the 1974-77
period and again during 1992 small quantities of natural rubber were
being exported. In general the policy has been one of promoting self-
sufficiency, and import substitution. Changes in stocks - an intermediate
and not a final expenditure category - arise due to production fluctuations,
government policy or a stock policy of manufacturers of rubber products.
Rubber demand is dominated by rubber consumption. In the period
1965-90 the share of consumption in the total demand comes very close
to 100%, and is even somewhat higher in some periods due to negative
stock formation.

In Figure 7.1 annual growth rates, both actual and 5-years moving

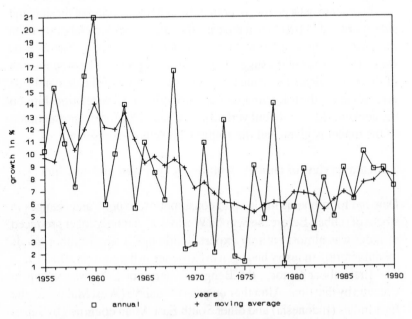

**Figure 7.1: Aggregate consumption of rubber
(growth rates in %)**

averages, of consumption of rubber are presented. Annual growth rates fluctuate tremendously. High growth rates are realised in 1960 (21%) and 1968 (16-17%) and low growth rates in 1975 and 1979 (1-2%). The average annual rate of growth of aggregate consumption of rubber is slightly below 10% in the most recent period (1985-1990). Average annual growth rates are relatively high at the end of the fifties and in the beginning of the sixties (10-15%), decreasing gradually to a low at the end of the seventies and the beginning of the eighties (somewhat above 5%), and recovering somewhat in the second half of the eighties.

The shares of natural rubber (NR), synthetic rubber (SR) and reclaimed rubber (RR) respectively in aggregate consumption of rubber seem to be relatively stable over time. Around 70% consists of natural rubber, 20% of synthetic rubber and 10% of reclaimed rubber (see Figure 7.2).

Rubber is consumed by manufacturers of rubber products. The ultimate purpose of this part is first to arrive at a model of aggregate consumption of rubber, which is rubber consumed by manufacturers of

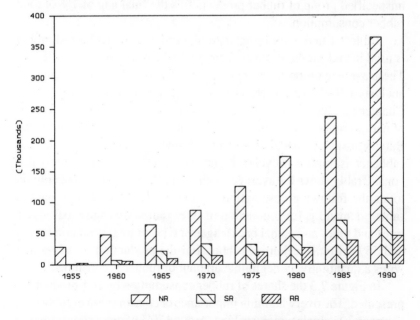

Figure 7.2: Consumption of natural rubber (NR), synthetic rubber (SR) and reclaimed rubber (RR)

rubber products and then to split this by type of rubber. Aggregate consumption of rubber is the sum total of the consumption of rubber by the end-products. The following distinction of rubber consumption by the end-products is available in Indian Rubber Statistics: automobile tyres and tubes, camel back, footwear, belts and hoses, latex foam, cables and wires, battery boxes, dipped goods; and others. We will take over this distinction with some adjustments with respect to the disaggregation of consumption of rubber for tyre and tube (see Chapter 8). In Table 7.1, data on the consumption of rubber by end-product are presented for the year 1991-92. The largest share is consumed by the tyre and tube producing manufacturers: around 64% of the combined domestic rubber consumption (1991-92) of natural, synthetic and reclaimed rubber, is absorbed by tyre and tube producers. We assume camel back - a retreading material - to be a part of rubber consumption for tyres and tubes. The remaining part is used by manufacturers of footwear (12%), belts and hoses (7%), latex foam and dipped goods (7%), battery boxes (2%) and cables and wires (less than 1%). An unspecified group of rubber products fills the final gap of 7% of total rubber consumption.

Table 7.1 makes clear that natural, synthetic and reclaimed rubber is used in end-products, on an average, in the proportions 70 : 20 : 10. These average proportions change somewhat over time, and a detailed analysis will allow us to detect a systematic pattern in these changes (see Chapter 8). Latex foam and dipped goods, however, are made entirely of natural rubber, reflecting the technical properties of these products. Battery boxes have a high content of reclaimed rubber (72%). Reclaimed rubber consumption in cycle tyres and tubes and cables and wires is also considerably above the average (both around 20%). In terms of column totals the following observations can be made: 64% of total natural rubber demand is for production of tyres (auto tyres and tubes, cycle tyres and tubes and camel back), against 65% of total synthetic rubber and 55% of total reclaimed rubber. For the production of cables and wires a quantitatively negligible amount of rubber is consumed.

In Figure 7.3 the shares of rubber consumption by end-product are presented. The overwhelming importance of consumption of rubber for commercial vehicle tyres is striking. Around 70% of rubber consumption

Table 7.1: Consumption of rubber according to end-product (1991- 92), tonnes

	NR	SR	RR	Total
Auto tyres and tubes	165,790	52,679	7,738	226,207
Cycle tyres and tubes	52,639	10,875	17,545	81,059
Camel back	26,747	5,320	3,450	35,517
Footwear	39,904	20,550	6,750	67,204
Belts and hoses	27,119	7,250	3,660	38,029
Latex foam	20,750	-	-	20,750
Cables and wires	1,120	1,055	570	2,745
Battery boxes	1,260	2,010	8,452	11,722
Dipped goods	17,067	-	-	17,067
Others	27,754	5,911	5,850	39,515
Total	380,150	105,650	54,015	539,815

(− = equal to 0; 0 = approximately 0)

	in % of column total				in % of row total		
	NR	SR	RR	Total	NR	SR	RR
Auto tyres and tubes	43.6	49.9	14.3	41.9	73.3	23.3	3.4
Cycle tyres and tubes	13.8	10.3	32.5	15.0	64.9	13.4	21.6
Camel back	7.0	5.0	6.4	6.6	75.1	15.0	9.7
Footwear	10.5	19.5	12.5	12.4	59.4	30.6	10.0
Belts and hoses	7.1	6.9	6.8	7.0	71.3	19.1	9.6
Latex foam	5.5	0.0	0.0	3.8	100.0	0.0	0.0
Cables and wires	0.3	1.0	1.1	0.5	40.8	38.4	20.8
Battery boxes	0.3	1.9	15.6	2.2	10.7	17.1	72.1
Dipped goods	4.5	0.0	0.0	3.2	100.0	0.0	0.0
Others	7.3	5.6	10.8	7.3	70.2	15.0	14.8
Total	100	100	100	100	70.4	19.6	10.0

for tyres and tubes, and more than 30% of total rubber consumption is used in the production of tyres and tubes for commercial vehicles. The share of rubber consumption for passenger car tyres and tubes is small (around 3%). This is caused primarily by the relatively small gross rubber use for passenger car tyres, the relatively small number of tyres per vehicle and, more recently, the down-sizing of tyres. The share of rubber consumption for bicycle tyres and tubes is, on the other hand, large (around 14%). This reflects the popularity of the bicycle as a general means of transport. The share of consumption of rubber for non-tyre end-products is around 35 percent. The number of units producing different types of products in India in 1991 is shown in Table 7.2. From this table it is clear that the tyre and tube producing industry is highly concentrated while the non-tyre sector consists of very large numbers of small production units.

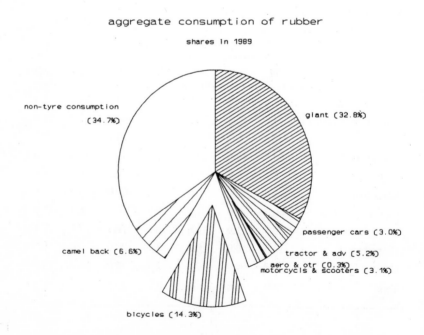

aggregate consumption of rubber

shares in 1989

non-tyre consumption (34.7%)

giant (32.8%)

passenger cars (3.0%)

camel back (6.6%)

tractor & adv (5.2%)

aero & otr (0.3%)
motorcycls & scooters (3.1%)

bicycles (14.3%)

Figure 7.3: Share of rubber consumption by end-product[1]

Table 7.2: Number of units producing rubber goods
at the end of 1991

Major tyre manufactures	24
Tyre, tubes and flaps	231
Auto and cycle parts	256
Foam products	348
Footwear	899
Moulded and extruded goods	806
Rubber bands	236
Sports goods	215
Tread rubber	602
Miscellaneous	1779
Total	**5249**

Note: Calculated total is higher as some manufacturers produce more than one
product.

Tyre and tube manufacturing

Some insight in the dynamics of rubber consumption can be gained by
analyzing developments in the aggregate production of tyres and tubes.

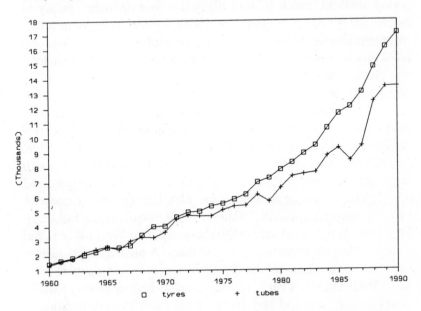

Figure 7.4: Production of tyres and tubes from 1960-1990

Figure 7.4 shows the increase in the production of tyres and tubes from 1960-90. Both sectors show an enormous growth, more or less *pari passu*. The annual average growth rate is around 8% both in tyres and in tubes.Table 7.3 shows the increase in the average annual rate of growth in specific parts of tyre and tube production. These figures show a decrease in growth rates in the seventies mainly due to the world recession and energy crisis during that period. The effect of increasing energy prices influences the tyre market both from the supply and the demand sides. On the supply side production costs of tyres rise as prices of some of the inputs of tyre production are closely related to energy prices. On the demand side the user costs of vehicles rise as the fuel cost for vehicles rises, and this might exert a downward pressure on use and sales and an upward pressure on discarding of vehicles. In particular, the production of passenger car tyres was severely hit during this period. Production of giant tyres shows a gradual decrease in growth rates over the entire period but seems hardly affected by fluctuations in energy prices. A substantial slow-down in growth rates is observed in tyres and tubes of agricultural tractors and animals drawn vehicles (ADV) in the period 1980-90, which is most likely due to a deliberate policy to discourage the use of tractors (see UNIDO, 1990). A major development over time seems to be the growing share of two-wheeler tyres and tubes production. In 1960 the share of production (in numbers) in total tyre production was less than 10% while it was around 40% in 1990. Since 1983, production of two-wheeler tyres shows a strong growth (around 15% annually), while the car tyre sector shows an upsurge in production in 1987 to 1990. The production of tyres and tubes for aeroplanes and off-the-road (OTR) vehicles is quantitatively negligible.

The tyre and tube industry can be broadly categorised into two segments viz., 'automobile tyres and tubes' and 'bicycle tyres and tubes'. The old major companies are M/s. Dunlop, M/s. Goodyear, M/s. Firestone (now M/s. Bombay Tyre International Ltd.) and M/s. India Super; they were all established before World War II and were then largely importing tyres and tubes. A big leap is production capacity took place in the 1960s when more companies viz., M/s. Goodyear, M/s. Ceat Tyres, M/s. Madras Rubber Factory (MRF), M/s. Premier Tyres and M/s. Inchek Tyres (now Tyre Corporation of

Table 7.3: Production of tyres and tubes in numbers
(annual average rate of growth in %)

	Giant	Passenger cars	2-wheeler	Tractor & ADV	Aero & OTR	Total
Tyres						
1960-1970	8.6	10.9	19.8	14.0	11.0	10.7
1970-1980	5.9	1.1	12.6	11.5	4.7	6.9
1980-1990	4.8	9.1	13.4	4.7	5.5	8.1
Tubes						
1960-1970	7.6	11.0	17.5	12.3	9.6	10.0
1970-1980	6.5	1.4	9.7	9.4	1.8	6.2
1980-1990	4.6	9.8	12.4	3.0	0.0	7.4

Table 7.4: Capacity and production of automobile tyres
(million nos.)

Year	1960	1965	1970	1975	1980	1985	1990
Installed capacity (1)	1.74	2.98	4.08	6.95	8.86	16.07	24.20
Production (2)	1.47	2.58	4.04	5.56	7.85	12.30	20.35
(2)/(1)*100	84.5	86.6	99.0	80.0	88.6	76.5	84.1

India) established their factories in various parts of the country. As a result the total production capacity of auto-tyres, which was 1.74 million in 1960 went up to 4.08 million numbers in 1970. Production of auto tyres increased during the period from 1.47 million to 4.04 million. During the 1970s substantial development of the automobile industry took place and the need for additional capacity for automobile tyres was found necessary.

New additions were M/s. MRF (Goa), M/s. Modi Rubber, M/s. Apollo Tyres, M/s. JK Tyres, M/s. Vikrant Tyres and M/s. Birla Tyres. The liberalisation of industrial policy, like abolition of industrial licences, easing up of import restrictions and promotion of exports in the 1980s lead to the rapid growth of the tyre industry. During the 1970s and the 1980s a number of small tyre units also came up for the manufacture of two and three wheeler tyres and tubes. The total installed capacity of automobile tyres, which at the end of 1980 was 8.86 million went up to 24 million in1990. During this period the output of tyres had increased from 7.85 million to 20.35 million. Total production capacity of all tyre companies during 1991 was estimated to be of the order of 30.0 million.

Indian tyre industry produces a variety of tyres and tubes ranging from animal drawn vehicles to aircraft tyres and specially designed tyres of defence vehicles. The indigenous requirement of tyres is fully met by Indian tyre companies. The size of tyres produced ranged from light weighted moped tyre to over one tonne giant earth mover tyre. At present there are about 60 tyre companies out of which 15 are producing truck and bus tyres. In all sub-markets the 5 largest companies had a market share of around 70% in 1988. The market share of the 10 largest companies was more than 95% in all sub-markets, except some quantitatively negligible parts of the tyre market (namely tyres of scooters, motorcycles, animal drawn vehicles and tractor front tyres; in the former two sub-markets Falcon and Srichakra have a substantial market share, in the latter two Metro has a substantial market share [see Rubber Trends (1989)]. Other manufacturing units are very small and produce two/three wheeler tyres/tubes only. Both in terms of turnover and of number of tyres produced MRF was the largest tyres company in 1990 [see Rubber Trends (1991)].

The tyre industry is geared for manufacture of tyres of required specifications of new vehicles on Indian roads e.g. Maruti, Contessa, etc. Many factories are small in size compared to the factories in the industrialised countries [see Modi (1988)]. Around 5% of the total production of tyres is now exported. However, bus and truck tyres had exports account for about 18% of the production in that category in 1990-91. In Figure 7.5 the development of the value of tyres and all rubber products exported is shown. The value of tyre exports in 1992 amounted to US$ 146 million, according to ATMA. Around 25% of truck and bus tyres produced were exported. There is an enormous incentive to export as imports financed with these foreign exchange earnings are to some extent exempt from import duty. Imports of tyres is negligible due to high import duty (145% in 1989). There is a decreasing substantial tax incidence on domestic prices of tyres and tubes: total taxes as a percentage of selling price is in the range of 45 to

66%, of which around 30 to 40% is on the output side, mainly excise duty, and 10 to 20% on the input side, mainly import duty (see Modi, 1988).

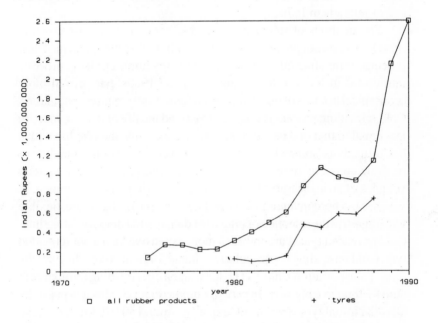

Figure 7.5: Value of exports of rubber products

Tyre Retreading

Tyre retreading is the process of recapping worn out tyres to prolong the life of the tyre. Some 85% of an average truck tyre of 50 kg. that is said to be worn out, will still be intact (see Ashokanand, 1988). Retreading of tyres is common in case of commercial vehicles and to a somewhat smaller extent in case of passenger cars and two- and three-wheelers. The number of retreads during a life time of a tyre differs. Tyres of commercial vehicles are retreaded around 5 to 8 times, tyres of passenger cars around 3 times, and tyres of two- and three- wheelers once, while motor cycle tyres are not retreaded. Retreading has gained economic significance in the light of high prices of tyres, especially truck/bus category. The total cost of retreading a tyre is a fraction of the cost of buying a new tyre. In case of commercial vehicles the costs of retreading a tyre are in between 10 to 20% of the cost of a new tyre (see Kuriakose, 1992). In case of passenger car tyres this percentage is slightly higher, namely around 25% (see Kurian, 1991). This explains the widespread use of retreads in India.

The methods of retreading available are conventional retreading (also known as hot process, mould cure or hot retreading) and the latest procured retreading (also known as cold retreading). The latter process, introduced in India in the beginning of the 1980s, has proved more economical in terms of tyre life after retreading and is gaining popularity. Cold retreading process is reported to extend the life of the tyre more or less equal to that of a new tyre in many cases, while the tyre life with a hot retreads is somewhat shorter. However, the average number of possible consecutive cold retreads is lower (5x in case of commercial vehicles) than in the case of conventional retreading (8x for commercial vehicles). The conventional retreading process is also more flexible with regard to the selection of injured or damaged casings for retreading. Cold retreaded tyre is around 30% more expensive than a hot retreaded tyre. Cold retreading is particularly suitable for radial tyres. In 1989 the State Transportation Units (STU) have taken up retreading through cold cure method in a big way. In case of commercial vehicles it is possible, after the initial tyre is worn cut (c.q. after around 50,000 km.), to make use of the original casing for another 160,000 km. applying 5 times consecutive cold retreading (5x 32,500) or 220,000 km. applying conventional retreating (8x 27,500 km.). It is estimated in an internal undated report on 'Retreading' by the Automobile Tyre Manufacturers Association that currently about 75% of all retreads are done with the conventional method. On an average a retread for a commercial vehicle (heavy and medium) requires 9.5 to 14 kg. of rubber, for a LCV 4.5 to 5.5 kg., for a passenger car 2 (Maruti) to 4.5 (Ambassador) kg. of rubber, and of a scooter 1 to 2 kg. of rubber. The demand for retreaded tyres of commercial vehicles accounts for 80% of the retread market.

The (conventional) retreading sector consists of a large number of small scale units, manufacturing tread rubber and tyre repair materials. Currently there are in operation some 3000 units with conventional retreading equipment, employing around 400,000 people (!!!) (see ATMA, op. cit.). The large number of firms in conventional retreading is largely the result of the tax structure (see Kurian, 1991, Kuriakose, 1992). In the procured retreading market four companies (MRF Ltd., Elgi Tyre and Tread Ltd., Indag Rubber Ltd. and Sunco Machines Ltd.) account for 93% of procured retreading. Retread rubber is distinguished in the data as a separate category of rubber consumption according to the end-product named camel back. The share of rubber consumption for camel back in total rubber consumption has been in between 4.8% and 7.1% in the period 1965-1989. In 1991-92 this share was 6.6%.

Manufacturing of vehicles[2]

The development of the tyre and tube industry is closely related to the development of the vehicle industry. For that reason some background is presented on the structure and developments of the various vehicle markets in India over the past 50 years. Government policy and its impact on the vehicle markets will be considered as well. In the description of specific markets a distinction is made between commercial vehicles [trucks, buses and light commercial vehicles (LCVs)], passenger cars (including jeeps), agricultural tractors and two and threewheelers (motorcycles, scooters, mopeds, three-wheelers). In Figure 7.6 the production of vehicles (four wheelers) is presented.'From Figure 7.6 it can be observed that ever since 1983 production levels of passenger cars have been growing rapidly with average annual growth rates of 17.5% (the Maruti phenomenon), while they showed a moderate growth of 4.5% in the preceding period. Commercial vehicle realised some speeding up of production levels in the period 1977 to 1981 (21% average annual growth), combined with more moderate rates of growth in the periods before and after (2.5% and 3.5% respectively). In case of agricultural tractors four periods can be distinguished: up to 1977, from 1977 to 1981, from 1981 to 1987 and 1987 onwards with growth rate being 8%, 24%, -1.5% and 19% respectively. In the aggregates, only in the case of passenger cars production shows some slow down during/ after the energy crises. In the early sixties around 50% of the total number of vehicles sold were commercial vehicles. This relatively high share declines to between 20 and 30% in more recent periods. In 1990 almost twice as many passenger cars as commercial vehicles were produced.

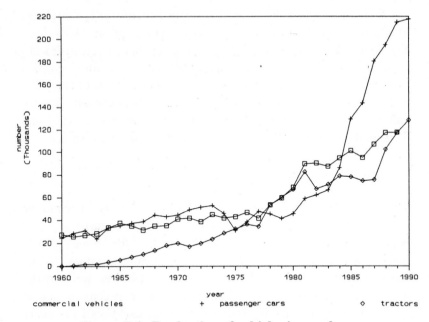

Figure 7.6: Production of vehicles in numbers

Government policy has played a major role in the developments in the vehicle sector: capacity licensing, foreign exchange allocation, restrictions on foreign collaborations and price control have been the operative factors at various points in time. Production of vehicles has been licensed almost since the First Five-Year Plan. Licences have been based on total demand, the national priorities and total supply. There has been a pronounced priority for commercial vehicles *vis-a-vis* passenger cars: after the Second Plan Period[3] no new passenger car units were allowed entry until 1982 (except Sipani Automobiles in a small way) and much larger capacities were sanctioned for commercial vehicles than for passenger cars (in particular in the Fifth and Sixth plans). Production capacity of two wheelers has been licensed as well ever since the First Plan period. In the Fourth and Fifth Plan periods, however, a substantial increase in licensed capacity of two-wheelers has taken place. Practically, this implied for the two-wheeler sector that capacity licensing hardly limited installing new capacity and entry of new firms, ever since the beginning of the seventies. Only new foreign collaborations (in the field of two-wheelers) have been restricted in this period. Nevertheless, no new domestic firms entered the market. The components supplying industry has been operating under comparable restrictions ever since the fifties. Licensing has contributed to create an effective barrier to entry in all segments of the market, with the notable exception of the scooter and moped segment. Besides of course, the highly ologopolistic market structure of most, if not all, segments of the market (see the final part of this section) contributed to this barrier to entry as well.

Ever since the fifties imports of complete vehicles have been totally restricted, as well as foreign exchange allocations for assemblers. Only in case of domestic programmes of firms to manufacture vehicles and availability of production facilities at these firms, foreign exchange allocations were considered. A policy has been enforced to create vehicle manufacturing capacity and all other required component manufacturing capability domestically. Surveys on foreign collaboration might give an impression of a vehicle manufacturing sector that is highly integrated with the world's leading vehicle producers and one that has incorporated a comparable standard of technology embodied in the vehicles produced. However, the opposite is true. Just a quick glance on an average Indian road will reveal that most vehicles currently being driven on Indian roads are old fashioned, and compare relatively poorly with world standards. In particular the technology to design new models has an extremely poor record (Narayana, 1989, p. 76.): only a few companies have shown the capability to develop new models with their own know-how.[4] On the whole foreign collaborations have been severely restricted: though there have been some differences in the policy stance in the period before 1984, the overall picture is one of almost total discouragement of foreign collaboration during this period. In all respects the restrictive policy has changed dramatically since 1983/1984[5]: the number of foreign collaborations approved in the years 1985 and 1986 has been higher than during the 25 previous years (see Narayana, 1989, p. 71)! The licensing system has been weakened and all sorts of regulations have been liberalised. During 1991 government liberalised the industrial policy further. Abolition of industrial licensing, automatic clearance of direct foreign investment up to 51% liberalisation of technology transfer agreements and collaborations etc., are some of the salient features of the new industrial policy.

Commercial vehicles

Three types of commercial vehicles can be distinguished, namely trucks, buses and light commercial vehicles. In Figure 7.7 a break-up of the production of commercial vehicles in these three types is presented. From the figure it can be observed - as pointed out before - that aggregate production levels accelerated in the period 1977 to 1981 (21% growth), combined with more moderate rates of growth in the periods before and after (2.5% and 3.5% respectively). From the break-up, however, a slightly more pronounced pattern emerges. The production of light commercial vehicles shows continuous rapid growth ever since the late seventies (16% growth), which was somewhat slower in the preceding period (10% growth). This segment of the market has been affected severely by the energy crises: the production level of 1973 could only be restored in 1978. In 1990 production of ICV's equals the production of trucks. The truck segment shows a stop-go development comparable to the production of agricultural tractors: sharp increases in production from 1977 to 1981 and from 1986 onwards respectively 19% and 14%, but slow or even negative growth in the remaining periods 5% and -4% respectively. Production of buses is the smallest segment ever since the eighties, and therefore the development is somewhat disguised in the graph. Closer inspection, however, reveals of extremely rapid growth in the mid-sixties, probably due to an increase in installed capacity, and moderate growth in the period to 1985 of 5%, but from 1985 onward a decrease in production levels (-4% being the average annual growth).

The development of market shares of the major vehicle companies for the period 1950 to 1990 shows a high concentration, although sometimes shifting between companies, in all the three segments over the entire period. Price controls have been effective till 1968 for commercial vehicles. Next to price controls, selling prices of commercial vehicles carry a substantial amount of tax. Fluctuation in tax rates do influence selling prices but have little connection with pricing policy of individual firms. However, between firms operating in the same market segment the impact of taxation will be equivalent.

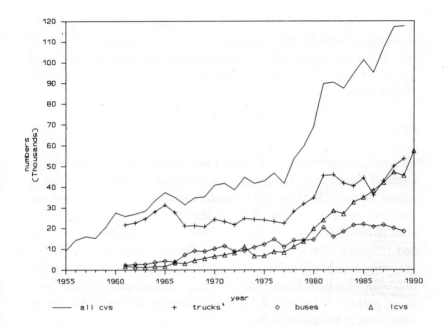

Figure 7.7: Production of types of commercial vehicles, in numbers

Passenger cars

The passenger car market is of considerable importance in terms of number of cars sold, but of substantially smaller importance in terms of rubber required for tyres and tubes (see Figure 7.3). This is mainly caused by the relatively low rubber content of passenger car tyres, but also by the average driving distance of passenger cars. In Figure 7.7 the production of passenger cars is presented. What is immediately striking is the enormous boost in production and sales since 1983. Up to 1983 the average annual growth rate is approximately 10%, from 1983 onwards the average annual growth rate is 22%. This is due to massive investments of the Maruti Udyog (MUL) factory, an investment with technical and financial participation of Suzuki, Japan, and made possible by the government policy of freely permitting technical and financial participation by foreign automobile manufacturers.

In 1982 MUL did not exist, but at the end of the eighties it had a share of around 60% of total sales of passenger cars in India! Production and sale of jeeps, numerically of moderate importance compared to commercial vehicles and passenger cars, grew constantly since 1976 with an average annual growth rate of around 14%, compared to around 5% in the period before 1976. Price controls have been effective till 1968 for jeeps and for passenger cars till 1974.

Agricultural tractors

The agricultural tractor market is of considerable importance both in terms of the number of vehicles sold, as well as in terms of the use of rubber for tyres. With respect to production of agricultural tractors we observe - as mentioned earlier - four periods: up to 1977, from 1977 to 1981, from 1981 to 1987 onwards, growth rate being 8%, 24%, 1.5% and 19% respectively (see Figure 7.6). Sources claim that 'due to the government policy to discourage the use of agricultural tractors in order to avoid a reduction of rural employment, production and sales stabilised in the period 1981-1987'. After 1987, however, the pre-1981 growth rates seem to be re-established.

Two and three-wheelers

Average annual rate of growth of production of two and three wheelers over the period 1956-1990 is 16%. Growth rates of production fluctuate less in the most recent period. The two- wheeler market is an important market so far as personal transport is concerned. Only the relatively well-to-do can afford a car, which leaves the two-wheeler as the most attractive and accessible transport options for the bigger part of the Indian population. In terms of rubber consumption for two-wheeler tyres and tubes, however, its importance is of a moderate size of around 4% (see Figure 7.4). Three categories of two-wheelers are distinguished: motorcycles, scooters and mopeds. Figure 7.8 shows the growth of production and sales. In all three cases the growth rates of production reach a low in the beginning of the eighties, after which growth rates increase again, to slow down again in the most recent period. Price controls have been effective for scooters till 1974. It is argued that capacity licensing in the two-wheeler segment in the past did not restrict investment in production capacity, though foreign companies were not allowed till the beginning of the eighties and hardly any new domestic companies entered the market.

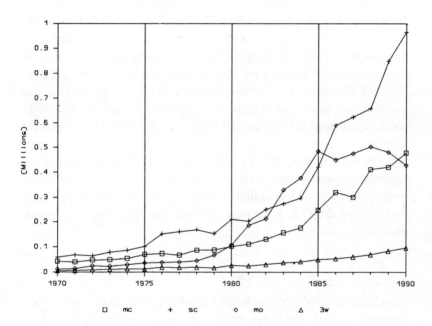

Figure 7.8: Production of two- and three-wheelers

Manufacturing of non-tyre rubber products

From Table 7.2 it is clear that a large number of all rubber products manufacturing units are manufacturing non-tyre rubber products: as many as 5000 medium scale and small scale units produce a wide range of different rubber products. The majority of production units are small scale units (more than 95%), accounting for nearly half of the total production. Non-tyre rubber products contain bicycle tyres and tubes, conveyor belting, rubber and canvas footwear, fan and v-belts, rubber hoses, and contraceptives. There is substantial foreign collaboration in this sector as well. There is some export of non-tyre rubber products.

The former USSR is the single largest export market and accounts for 60% of the total exports (see Rubber Trend, 1990).

7.3 Modelling consumption of rubber

In this section we give a short overview of the relationships on the demand side. As mentioned before export demand will be dealt with in Chapter 10 after to explaining the various relationships we will indicate if these relationships are of a technical, definitional or behavioral nature. We will also indicate if time-series data of respective variables are available, or need to be constructed, or simply guessed. In view of the forecasts we need to know as well which variables are exogenous to the model.

The final purpose of this part of the book is to arrive at a model of aggregate consumption of rubber. Aggregate consumption of rubber is constituted by the consumption of rubber according to the end-product. Starting the same as a formula we have the following definitional equation[6]:

$$C = \sum C_i$$

It is assumed that the consumption of rubber is derived demand. Actual demand relates to the final products in the manufacture of which rubber is used. In some cases these products coincide with the rubber product itself (for example footwear). A distinction of rubber consumption according to end-products enables us, thus, to develop demand relationships. As mentioned in Table 7.1 we do have data on the consumption of rubber by the end-products. The following categories of end-products are distinguished in the Indian Rubber Statistics: automobile tyres and tubes all; cycle tyres and tubes, camel back, footwear, belts and hoses, latex foam, cables and wires, battery boxes, dipped goods, and others. Two major adjustments are made with respect to these categories. These adjustments are made only with the purpose of arriving at meaningful categories of rubber consumption.

In modelling the various end-uses of rubber the following three major components of rubber consumption are distinguished and will be treated separately:

- tyres and tubes of vehicles;
- retreading;
- non-tyre end-products;

Consumption of rubber for tyres and tubes for vehicles is determined by the demand for tyres and tubes, part of which consists of replacement of worn out tyres, while another part is used for new vehicles. Original equipment demand is determined by production of vehicles (in numbers), the average number of tyres per vehicle and the average gross use of rubber (in kg.) in the production of a tyre or a tube. Replacement demand is determined technically by the average gross use of rubber per tyre, the average number of tyres per vehicle, the number of vehicles in use and the frequency of replacement. This frequency of replacement depends on the average driving distance per year per vehicle and the average tyre distance. For each type of vehicle the number of vehicles in use can be determined with the help of a single vintage approach. The number of vehicles in use is make up of all vehicles sold in earlier years less the vehicles taken out of use, or, which is equivalent to the former, the number of vehicles in use in the current period is made up of the number of vehicle sales in the current and all previous periods, less the current scrappage of all earlier vintages. The life-time of vehicles is assumed to be entirely technically determined, due to the relatively low cost of repair services. Finally, sales of vehicles is determined as the outcome of supply of and demand for vehicles. Per capita demand for new vehicles is determined by per capita income (GDP) and relative prices. Other variables - the number of vehicles in use relative to the desired number of vehicles, nominal or real lending rates as a measure of credit availability; and, in some cases, petrol prices relative to consumer prices - seem to qualify as the determinants of the demand for vehicles.

Demand for retreading material is related with some lag to the number of vehicles in use, followed by the frequency of retreading, the number of tyres per vehicle, and the retreading material required for a specific type of tyre.

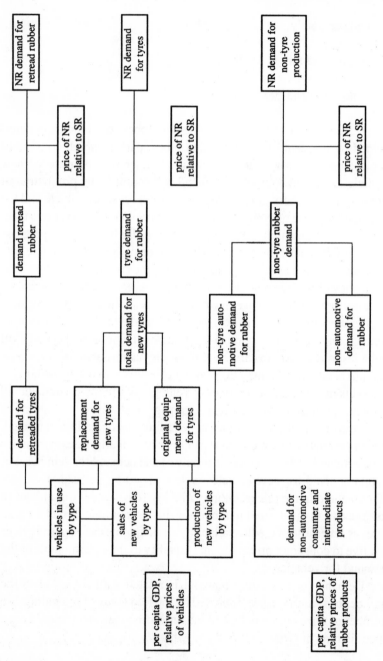

With respect to non-tyre end-products it is assumed that supply is determined by demand. Per capita demand for rubber for non- tyre end-products is determined by the per capita GDP and the relative prices.

The break up of the total demand for rubber for groups of end-products into demand by type of rubber (natural, synthetic and reclaimed) depends on relative prices and some autonomous developments. Details are described at the end of the next chapter.

The flow chart on page 122 summarises the main causalities on the demand side.

NOTES

1   In Indian writings on rubber it is customary to label consumption of (bi)cycle tyres and tubes as non-tyre consumption. Because of the modelling of consumption by end-product we deviate from this custom and label it as a separate category. For consumption of rubber for camel back the same is true. ADV = animal drawn vehicle; OTR = off-the-road; giant tyres are commercial vehicle tyres (tyres of trucks and buses).

2   This section is based on UNIDO (1990) and Narayana (1989).

3   Planning periods in India are:

I	1951/52-1955/56;	II	1956/57-1960/61;
III	1961/62-1965/66	IV	1969/70-1973/74;
V	1974/75-1978/79;	VI	1980/81-1984/85;
VII	1985/86-1989/90;	VIII	1992/93-1996/97.

4   In particular TELCO and BAL have introduced indigenously developed models (see Narayana, 1989, p. 21). With respect to new models it is concluded that 'all the other vehicle manufacturers were heavily dependent on foreign collaborators for introducing even minor changes'.

5   This policy change had already at the end of the seventies and the beginning of the eighties, but gained momentum halfway through the eighties.

6   Time subscripts are omitted if possible; i refers to the respective types of end-products distinguished (see the beginning of this section).

8

EMPIRICALLY MODELLING TYRE AND NON-TYRE RUBBER DEMAND

8.1 Introduction

In this chapter we develop a framework to analyze the distinctive components of demand. This is followed by the empirical results of the model. The outcome of the results yeiled by the model are compared with actual developments. Two components of demand for rubber, namely demand for retreading material and non-tyre demand, do not fit in this framework and are given a simpler treatment. Finally, rubber consumption will be split into NR and SR. Part of some sections are rather technical in nature, requiring knowledge of econometrics for a proper understanding. The layman in this respect may prefer to skip such parts knowing that all that is being done here is to explain the sales of means of transportation, demand for tyres and tubes and for rubber generally, largely in terms of income, population, past sales and prices, along the lines of the scheme described at the end of Chapter 7. This serves as a tool to make forecasts for the demand items, which will be treated in Chapter 10.

8.2 Rubber consumption for tyres and tubes

Consumption of rubber for tyres and tubes depends on the production of tyres and tubes. Supply of tyres and tubes in India is equal to the domestic production: tyres and tubes are not imported. Demand for tyres and tubes is dominated by domestic consumption. Exports of tyres and tubes and, in general, exports of manufactured rubber goods, have been negligible in the past and are therefore neglected in the current framework.[1] In constructing projections, however, this assumption can be relaxed. The number of tyres and tubes traded in the market will be the result of supply and demand of tyres and tubes. We assume that production of tyres and tubes is not restricted, and is entirely determined by demand. An estimated 70% to 80% of all tyres produced are used for replacement of worn out tyres, the remaining part is used for new vehicles. For the consumption of rubber for tyres and tubes we also make this distinction. In terms of a formula we have, by definition:

$$C_{tt} = C_{tt,oed} + C_{tt,rd} \tag{8.1}$$

where $C_{tt,}$ = consumption of rubber for tyres and tubes;
$C_{tt,,oed}$ = consumption of rubber for tyres and tubes: original equipment demand;
$C_{tt,rd}$ = consumption of rubber for tyres and tubes: replacement demand

Original equipment demand is determined by multiplying the production of vehicles (in numbers) with the average number of tyres per vehicle and the average gross use of rubber (in kg.) in the production of a tyre or tube. Stated as a formula this technical relationship reads:[2]

$$C_{tt,oed} = \overline{rwt} * qv * \overline{ntv} \tag{8.2}$$

where rwt = gross rubber weight of a vehicle tyre;
qv = production of vehicles in numbers;
ntv = number of tyres per vehicle including a spare tyre

Replacement demand for rubber for automobile tyres and tubes is determined technically by multiplying average gross use of rubber per tyre with the number of vehicles in use, the average number of tyres per vehicle and a replacement factor. This replacement factor is equal to the average driving distance per year per vehicle divided by the average tyre distance. Stated as formula we have:

$$C_{tt,\,rd} = \overline{rwt} * \overline{dd/td} * \overline{viu} * (\overline{ntv} - 1) \tag{8.3}$$

where rwt = gross rubber weight of a vehicle tyre;
td = tyre distance;

dd   = driving distance per year per vehicle
viu = vehicles in use;
ntv = number of tyres per vehicle including a spare tyre;

The number of vehicles in use is made up of the number of vehicles in use in the previous period, plus the sales, and minus the vehicles not anymore in use, both with reference to the current period:

$$\text{viu} = \text{viu}_{t-1} + \text{sv} - \text{ascrap} \qquad (8.4)$$

where viu   = vehicles in use
         sv   = sales of vehicles
         ascrap = scrappage summed over vintage in year t

or, which is equivalent to the former, the number of vehicles in use in the current period is made up of the number of vehicle sales in the current and all past periods, less the current and past scrappage of all vintages.

$$\text{viu} = \sum \text{sv}_{t-j} - \sum \sum \text{scrap}_{t-i,t-j} \qquad (8.5)$$

where scrap = scrappage of vintage t-j in a year t-i

Adding up scrappage per vintage over the past years simplifies the equation. If then states that the number of vehicles in use is the sum of what is left of current and past vintages.

$$\begin{aligned} \text{viu} &= \sum \text{sv}_{t-j} - \sum \text{cscrap}_{t-j} \\ &= \sum (\text{sv}_{t-j} - \text{cscrap}_{t-j}) \end{aligned} \qquad (8.6)$$

where cscrap = scrappage summed over years of a particular
                      vintage t-j

The share of scrapped vehicles per vintage is assumed to follow a logistic function, with a certain average length of life and a 'skewness' factor as parameters. In formula:

$$\text{SHARE}(\text{cscrap}_{t-j}) = 1/\{1+e^{((\mu-t)/\alpha\mu)}\} \qquad (8.7)$$

where μ = average length of life;
       α = 'skewness' factor

With reference to the relative scarcity of capital in India - indeed, vehicles can be considered to be capital goods, or consumer durables - this approach is acceptable. Given the relatively low cost of repair services, the relative user cost of capital cannot be considered to be a substantial reason to scrap vehicles: consequently the life-time of vehicles will be determined entirely technically and not economically. For some vehicle types the average life of vehicles is assumed to follow a trend development as the results of technical change. Details on these issues are presented in the sections on the respective types of vehicles.

The final step is to model the demand and supply of vehicles. Our interest of course is both in production and in sales: production determines original equipment demand for tyres, and sales contribute to the vehicle population, and thus to the replacement demand for tyres. An approach in which both supply and demand equations are estimated seems most appropriate. However, as is clear from our description of economic policy *vis-a-vis* the vehicle markets (see section 8.2), both prices and quantities were regulated by the government till fairly recently. These regulations are related to the five-year plans.

Price controls have only been lifted in 1968 for commercial vehicles and jeeps, and for scooters and passenger cars in 1974. Only in the beginning of the eighties a start has been made to do away with capacity licensing and to liberalise all sorts of regulations: Capacity licensing has been abandoned after 1985. In the two-wheeler market, however, capacity licensing has probably been ineffective after 1974. The following table summarises the price and quantity restrictions in the vehicle markets.

Table 8.1: Restrictions in vehicle markets

	Prices	Quantities
Commercial vehicles	till 1968	till 1980-1985
Jeeps	till 1968	till 1980-1985
Passenger cars	till 1974	till 1980-1985
Agricultural tractors		till 1980-1985
Two-wheelers	till 1974 (scooters)	probably ineffective

Despite these restrictions demand equations for (sales of) vehicles by type of vehicle have been estimated: for the respective vehicle markets it is assumed that in the long run production will adjust to demand. Initially we start estimating these behavioural equations with a simple specification: per capita demand for new vehicles is determined by the per capita GDP and relative prices. Relative prices are prices of vehicles relative to average consumer prices. As a formula this reads:

$$sv_{k,pc} = sv_{k,pc} (gdppc, p_{v,k}/p_c) \tag{8.8}$$

where sv_k =   sales of vehicles of type k;
       $gdppc$ =   per capita gross domestic product;
       $p_{v,k}$ =   price of vehicle of type k;
       p_c =   price of consumer goods

In the literature several additional explanatory variables are proposed: the number of vehicles in use relative to the desired number of vehicles (see Chow, 1983; F.T. Juster and P. Wachtel, 1972); nominal or real lending rates as a measure of credit availability; and, in some cases, petrol prices relative to consumer products in general. The personal income distribution is expected to have an impact on demand for vehicles as well (see F. Jorgenson and T. Wentzel-Łarsen, 1990). Estimation of substitution effects by means of the prices of one type of vehicle relative to prices of another particular type of vehicle has been omitted altogether. Partly this has been done because substitution is highly questionable in some cases (one can hardly assume substitution between, for example, trucks and scooters), and partly (in cases in which substitution seemed plausible) because price series hardly differed. Some of these variables have been experimented with as well. Some other variables do qualify to be used in estimating demand equations but were not used due to lack of (reliable) data.

The above framework applies to rubber consumption for tyres and tubes of most types of vehicles, and, in a slightly modified way, to rubber consumption for bicycle tyres and tubes.

Rubber consumption for retreading

The process of renewing that part of a tyre which is worn out is called retreading. Retread rubber comprises a category of rubber consumption according to end-product called camel back. Demand for retreading material is related with some lag to the number of vehicles in use. Formally we have the following relationship:

$$C_{retreading} = \sum \overline{ntv}_k * retrr_k * \overline{rwrm}_k * viu_k \qquad (8.9)$$

where   k   =   type of vehicle;
        retrr   =   retreading rate (or the reciprocal of the number of times a tyre is retreaded);
        rwrm   =   rubber weight of retreading material per retreaded tyre;

As will become clear in the empirical part, the data requirements of this equation are far beyond the possibilities offered by our data-set.

Rubber consumption for non-tyre products

Non-tyre end-products comprise battery boxes, belts and hoses, footwear, latex foam and dipped goods, cables and wires and others. We do not elaborate an extensive framework, but estimate demand equations directly. The behavioural equation reads:

$$C_{nt,i} = C_{nt,i}(gdppc, p_{cnt,i}/p_c) \qquad (8.10)$$

where $C_{nt,i}$ =   consumption of rubber for non-tyre end-product i;
        $p_{cnt,i}$ =   price of non-tyre rubber end-product i.

From total rubber consumption to NR consumption

With the above framework we have derived estimates of total consumption of rubber, distinguished by categories of end-products and reflecting long run developments. What determines the share of NR in the production of these rubber goods? And, is it required to explain the NR share in consumption on an aggregated or a desegregated level? Producers of rubber products are able to react relatively fast to changes in the price of natural rubber relative to synthetic rubber.[3] Of course, the possibilities to substitute on economic grounds are restricted for technical reasons. For a number of reasons disaggregation in consumption of rubber by end-product seems appropriate, in determining the share of NR consumption in total consumption. The actual shares of NR diverge substantially between end-products, as is confirmed by simple inspection of the data (see Table 7.1 in Chapter 7). Going through the list of end-products it is also clear that these end-products concern products with highly different qualities, technical requirements and standards, and are produced by companies with a wide range of technical capabilities, capital and scale (see also Chapter 7). Both technical and economic differences in NR shares seem very likely. Hence, an analysis on a desegregated level is required. The share of consumption of natural rubber in total consumption, desegregated by consumption category, is explained by technology and relative prices. The estimated regression equation of this relationship can be used to calculate natural rubber demand by end-product and by type of rubber. Subsequently, these estimates of consumption by end-product of natural rubber are aggregated over end-products to generate total natural rubber consumption.

The price of reclaimed rubber (RR) is far below that of both synthetic (SR) and natural rubber (NR), as can be seen from Figure 8.1. On the basis of this huge price difference it is postulated that there will be no economic substitution between RR and NR or SR: reclaimed rubber will be used in the production of rubber goods as much as is technically possible. Although the market price of NR on the whole seems to be lower than the market price of SR there will be some substitution between NR and SR: this is explained by the fluctuating relative availability, which also will be reflected in the relative price. Empirically the share of NR[4] is estimated with the relative price of natural versus synthetic rubber, the lagged dependent variable and, in some cases, a trend variable (representing change in technology) as explanatory variables. Technical requirements and other influences are controlled by including a constant term and a trend variable in the regression.

The following regression equation is estimated:

$$c_{i,nr}/c_i = c_{i,nr}/c_i [(c_{i,nr}/c_i)_{t-1}, (p_{nr}/p_{sr})_{t-1}, \text{trend}] \qquad (8.11)$$

where $c_{i,nr}$ = consumption of NR in the production of good i;

c_i = consumption of all rubber in the production of good i;

p_{nr}/p_{sr} = price of NR relative to price of SR

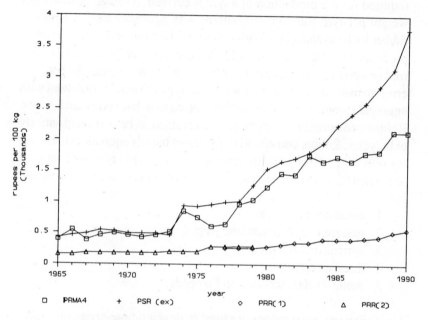

Figure 8.1: Prices of different types of rubber

Source: Rubber Board, NCAER

Note: The price of NR is the market price of RMA4; in case of SR a weighted average price of all types of synthetic rubber (SBR, PB, butyl) is calculated.

8.3 Data

The possibility to specify the developed framework empirically depends on the availability of data. The purpose of this section is to report on the most important data sources, to explain procedures to construct series, and to explain some assumptions made in creating data, as well as in forecasting. In treating these subjects we will attempt to follow the variables of equations (8.1) to (8.11).

Data on rubber consumption for tyres and tubes, distinguished by original equipment demand and replacement demand (equation 8.1) do not exist, and have to be derived. Hence, this break-up cannot be confirmed by observation. In equation (8.2) average gross rubber use required for the production of a tyre is derived. Average gross rubber weight per tyre should be consistent with aggregate consumption of rubber for tyres and tubes. With the help of the number of tyres and tubes produced by type, and using ATMA figures (see ATMA, 1990) on the rubber weight per tyre as a starting point, an attempt is made, by trial and error, to make the average tyre weight by type of vehicle consistent with aggregate consumption of rubber for automobile tyres and tubes. Rubber consumption for cycle tyres and tubes can be attributed entirely to bicycles. Rubber consumption for camel back is equivalent to rubber for retreading. Rubber consumption for automobile tyres and tubes is attributed to types of vehicles. Five types of vehicles are distinguished:

1. commercial vehicles;
2. passenger cars (including jeeps);
3. agricultural tractors;
4. three wheelers;
5. motor cycles, scooters and mopeds.

The following assumptions are used to develop time-series on rubber consumption for tyres and tubes for these specific types of vehicles:

- cross-ply and radial tyres are assumed to require more or less the same quantity of rubber;
- the technique of manufacturing tyres is assumed to be fixed over time with respect to the gross use of rubber. Smit (1982, p. 193) concludes on this issue: '... the statistics (of the weight of various types of tyres) indicate that there is considerable variation among countries but not much variation over time except for such countries as the USA in recent years';
- with respect to the average gross rubber weight, which is the gross rubber requirement in the production of a vehicle tyre, the following assumptions are made[5]:

*   passenger car tyres: 4.6 kg. (with a correction for down-sizing);
*   commercial vehicles tyres: 24.7 kg. (with a correction for lcv's);
*   agricultural tractors: 5.9 (front) and 32.5 (rear);
*   trailers and animal drawn vehicles: 6.7 kg.;
*   aero: 13.7 kg. and off-the-road; 90 kg.; and
*   motorcycles, three-wheeler, scooter and moped tyres: 2.1 kg.

-   a slight adjustment is made for the use of rubber required for the production of tubes by type of vehicle;

Time-series on the production of vehicles (equation 8.2) by type of vehicle are available. The average number of tyres per vehicle (equation 8.2) depends on the type of vehicle. Time-series on this variable are not available. However, an intuitively appealing 'guess' seems to be possible and will be fairly accurate, at least in most cases. Details on the numerical values of these variables are presented in the sections on the respective types of vehicles. Time-series on average tyre distance and average driving distance (equation 8.3) do not exist but we do have some fragmentary information, on which a 'reasonable' guess has been based. In fitting the framework to the observations, average tyre weight, average number of tyres, average driving distance and average tyre distance are assumed to be constant over time, to begin with. However, in some cases trend developments or shocks are introduced to improve the fit of the model. Indeed, whether fixing these variables over time is acceptable depends on the level of disaggregation, the homogeneity of the distinguished types of vehicles and the period considered. With a substantial spread of rubber weight per tyre, tyre distance, driving distance and number of tyres per vehicle over subgroups of a specific type of vehicle, say commercial vehicles, a shift in the relative size of these subgroups will have a considerable impact on variables that are fixed in our analysis (c.q. average driving distance, average tyre distance, average gross use, average number of tyres). There are good reasons to assume that this composition effect is, in some cases, substantial (see Smit, 1982, section 5.4). However, limited availability of data, in particular with respect to data on registered vehicles by type, force us to follow second best options in some cases. Particulars will be treated in the following sections. The choices made in desegregation are not without consequences: accurate projections hinge to a large extent on a proper desegregation. For each type of vehicle the number of vehicles in use (equation 8.3) is determined with the help of a simple vintage approach. Data on sales of vehicles by type of vehicle (equations 8.4 to 8.6, and 8.8) are available. Scrappage is determined by using the vehicle-type and vintage specific share of scrapped vehicles: economically this implies that deterioration is entirely technical in character. Gross domestic product, consumer prices and prices of vehicles and rubber products (equation 8.8 to 8.10) are to a large extent observed.

On an annual basis data on NR/SR/RR shares of the distinguished demand categories do not correspond fully with categories distinguished in the model used in this chapter. In particular, consumption of rubber for the production of automotive tyres and tubes is not distinguished by type of vehicle and type of rubber (see Table 8.2). This, however, is a minor problem: most tyre producers in India produce all types, or at least an extensive range of types of tyres,[6] and thus decisions about the share of NR will be taken for the entire automotive tyre and tube sector. In explaining the shares of NR/SR/RR the categories distinguished in the data are taken over with a few exceptions.[7] The share of NR/SR/RR in a specific end-product can be explained on technical and economic grounds. The former refers to technical requirements of specific end-products. Some products only allow a specific content of either NR, SR and RR. Apart from latex foam and dipped goods, which are 100% NR products,[8] there is little information on these technical requirements. The latter, the economic ground, refers to the impact of price difference between NR, SR and RR. In Figure 8.1 the price of 100 kg. of different types of rubber in the period 1965-1990 is plotted. The price of NR refers to the price of RMA4, as this is the grade of natural rubber that is produced most (and as all other grades, except latex, follow the price of RMA4). The price of SR is a weighted average of different types of SR,[9] with their shares in total SR production as weights. The price of RR is taken from two sources, namely NCAER [PRR(1)] and the Rubber Board [PRR (2)].

Table 8.2: Model and data desegregation of consumption of rubber by end-use

	model Chapter 7	available statistics
Tyres and tubes of commercial vehicles	x	
Tyres and tubes of passenger cars	x	
Tyres and tubes of agricultural tractors	x	x
Tyres and tubes of three-wheelers	x	
Tyres and tubes of two-wheelers	x	
Tyres and tubes of bicycles	x	x
Retreading/camel back	x	x
Latex foam		x
Dipped goods	x	x
Footwear	x	x
Belts and hoses	x	x
Battery boxes	x	x
Cables & wires		x
Others	x	x

Most data are from the Indian Rubber Statistics (IRS, several issues) or were supplied by the Rubber Board. Variables on the vehicle markets, some of which are reported in IRS, are taken from the Ministry of Industry, Government of India, the Ministry of Shipping and Transport, Monthly Statistics on Foreign Trade, Automotive Component Manufacturers India, New Delhi and Motor Transport Statistics of India. National variables are taken from the National Accounts Statistics and the Economic Surveys, Central Statistical Organisation (CSO), Government of India.

Demand equations are estimated with an estimation procedure called error correction. In a simplified way this procedure consists of distinguishing between the long run and the short run. Regression equations are estimated in two steps: first the long run equation in levels is estimated, followed by the short run equation in first differences. In the short run equation, the error of the long run equation, one period -

the so called error-correction - is added as an argument. In our estimations per capita GDP determines the long run path and price developments and dummies the short run. In some cases sample periods are truncated due to a lack of data, or doubtful estimation results.

8.4 The commercial vehicle market

Traditionally an important type of vehicle in terms of number of vehicles sold and produced is the commercial vehicle. In the early sixties around 50% of the total number of vehicles sold were commercial vehicles. This relatively high share declines to between 20% and 30% in more recent periods, due to the boost in sales of passenger cars. Over time a continuous growth can be observed in the period 1955-1990 with an average annual growth rate of 7.8%. In particular the late seventies and the beginning of the eighties show high growth rates. Production has hardly been affected by the oil-crises.

In line with the flow chart of section 7.3 in which the main causalities are summarised, demand equations for commercial vehicles have been estimated. The demand for new vehicles is determined by per capita GDP and relative prices (c.q. prices of vehicles relative to average consumer prices). Next, some experiments have been undertaken with nominal and real lending rates, as a measure of credit availability, petrol prices, and desired number of commercial vehicles relative to actual number of commercial vehicles in use. As explained above a long run relationship with per capita GDP is estimated and deviations from this long run path are used in a short run equation. After numerous attempts the following relationship captures fluctuation in per capita sales best:

$$dls_{cv,pc} = 1.46 - .42 * dlrp_{cv} - .52 * (ls_{cv,pc,t-1} - 1.31 - .73 * lgdppc_{t-1})$$
$$\phantom{dls_{cv,pc} =} (6.5) \ (3.1) (5.2) \phantom{* (ls_{cv,pc,t-1} -} (6.5) \ (13.2)$$
$$\phantom{dls_{cv,pc} =} -.20 * d74 - .21 * d77 + .19 * d81$$
$$\phantom{dls_{cv,pc} =} (3.4) (3.5) (3.5)$$

$R2$ = .67; 24 observation; 1966-1989; (absolute) t-values in parentheses.

where $s_{cv,pc}$ = per capita sales of commercial vehicles
        rp_{cv} = price of commercial vehicles deflated with cpi
        $gdppc$ = per capita gross domestic product is constant
                    prices (1980=100)

(variables are transformed in first differences of logs: a 'd' before a variable-name stands for a first difference and an '1' for natural log).

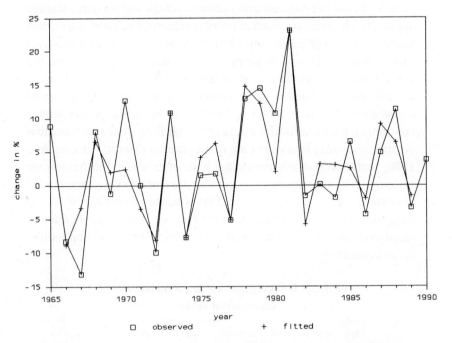

Figure 8.2: Sales of commercial vehicles: observed and fitted

With respect to the estimation results the following comments must be made. Some dummies (1974, 1977 and 1981) were required to take account of outliers. Estimation results point at an elasticity with respect to per capita GDP of .73 and with respect to relative prices of -.41. A graph has been plotted with observed and fitted values (see Figure 8.2). Forecasts for the period 1990-2020 are reported in Chapter 10.

Number of commercial vehicles in use

So called original equipment demand (oed) for tyres, and thus for rubber, is determined by the production of vehicles. In forecasting it is assumed that production of vehicles adjusts to the demand for vehicles.

Replacement demand (rd) — the other component of demand for rubber — is determined by the number of vehicles in use. The number of vehicles in use is estimated using sales of vehicles applied in a vintage approach. The average length of life of commercial vehicles is assumed to start at a level of 20 years in 1950 and to move slowly upwards over time to reach a value of 30 years in 1990. Figures 8.3 to 8.4 show the calculated as well as the registered number of commercial vehicles in use and the calculated vintage composition in 1990. The number of registrations has been lifted upward over the entire period with a constant number to allow for trucks and buses for military purposes that do appear in sales figures but are not registered (Motor Vehicles Act, 1988, section 60). From Figure 8.3 it is inferred that the framework systematically generates a lower number of vehicles in use compared to the number of registered vehicles. This is due to inconsistencies in the data: from Table 8.3 it is clear that for a number of years the increase in registered vehicles is higher than sales, which should be impossible, given equation 8.4.

Table 8.3: Change in registration and sales of commercial vehicles

	1980	1981	1982	1983	1984	1985	1986	1987	1988	1989	1990	1991
Δ registr. (1)	36	68	70	75	90	82	111	93	132	·158	142	179
sales (2)	68	88	89	91	91	99	97	104	119	117	124	138
(2) – (1)	32	20	19	16	1	17	-14	11	-13	-41	-18	-41

Weight, tyre distance, driving distance and number of tyres

Next, we need to have numerical values for average gross rubber weight of a commercial vehicle tyre, average tyre distance of commercial vehicles, average driving distance per year per commercial vehicle, and average number of tyres per commercial vehicle, in order to calculate consumption of rubber for replacement demand of tyres. The homogeneity requirement is violated in case of commercial vehicles. A broad range of vehicles fall under the heading of commercial vehicles (light, medium and heavy trucks, buses), with widely differing loading

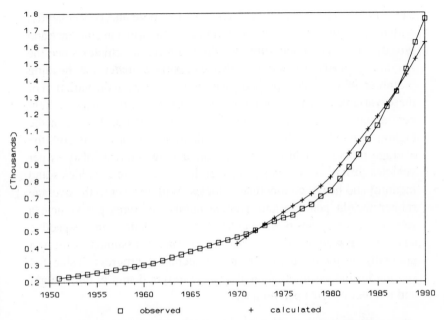

Figure 8.3: Commercial vehicles in use (calculated and observed)

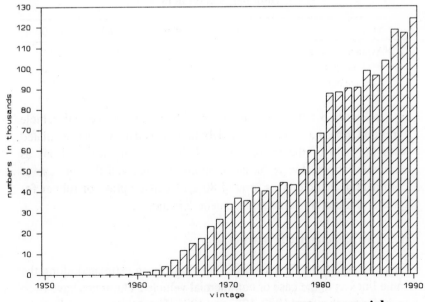

Figure 8.4: Calculated vintage composition of commercial vehicles in 1990

capacities for a large spectrum of transport-functions and, consequently, with much variation in number of tyres per vehicle, driving distance and tyre distance. The popularity of light commercial vehicles since the beginning of the seventies - also categorised under the heading 'commercial vehicles' - probably causes an increase in the variation of these variables. In the beginning of the seventies the share of light commercial vehicles was around 15% to 20%, and at the end of the eighties around 40%. It seems desirable to adjust for this as both the average rubber weight of tyres and the average number of tyres per vehicles differs considerably between light commercial vehicles and medium and heavy commercial vehicles. With respect to the average rubber weight per tyre and average number of tyres per vehicle a weighted average has been calculated, with the share of the respective categories as weights. The average tyre distance is assumed to follow a gradually rising trend as a result of technical progress. Table 8.4 summaries the assumptions with respect to tyre distance, tyre weight and number of tyres per vehicle.

Table 8.4: Average tyre distance, tyre weight and number of tyres of cv's

Year	1960	1970	1980	1990
Average tyre weight	25.7	25.7	23.2	22.3
Average tyre distance	52000	53000	54000	55000
Average number of tyres	7	7	7	7

In Figure 8.5 the consumption of rubber for commercial vehicle tyres and tubes has been presented, both observed as well as calculated with the help of the framework and the necessary assumptions as explained above. From the calculations it is derived that in case of commercial vehicle tyres around 80% of consumption of rubber for tyres and tubes concerns replacement demand.

8.5 The passenger car market

Demand equations for passenger cars have been estimated along the same lines as in the case of commercial vehicles. Dummies have been included for the years 1979, 1983 and 1985. The estimation result reads:

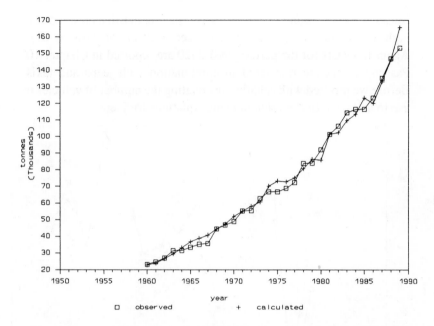

Figure 8.5: Consumption of rubber for commercial vehicle tyres and tubes

$$\text{dls}_{pc,pc} = 3.76 - 1.12 * \text{dlrp}_{pc} - .27 * (\text{ls}_{pc,pc,t-1} - 3.76 - 2.26 * \text{lgdppc}_{t-1})$$
$$\quad\; (4.9)\;\; (4.3) \qquad\quad (3.0) \qquad\qquad\qquad (4.9)\;\; (4.4)$$
$$\quad -.19 * \text{d79} -.34 * \text{d83} + .26 * \text{d85}$$
$$\quad\;\;\, (1.5) \qquad (2.4) \qquad\quad (1.9)$$

$R^2 = .68$; 18 observations; 1972-1989; (absolute) t-values in parentheses

where $s_{pc,pc}$ =   per capita sales of passenger cars
        rp_{pc} =   price of passengers cars deflated with cpi
        gdppc   =   per capita gross domestic product in constant
                         prices (1980=100)

(variables are transformed in first differences of logs: a 'd' before a variable-name stands for a first difference and an 'I' for natural log).

Estimation results show a significant price-elasticity of -1.12. Both the value and the significance of this price-elasticity depend to a large extent on one observation (1975). Nominal and real lending rates did not prove to add to the explanation. Elasticity with respect to per capita income is as high as 2.26. A graph has been plotted with observed and

fitted values (see Figure 8.6). Although the income elasticity is somewhat
high, this equation nevertheless has been used in forecasts as well.
Again forecasts for the period 1990-2020 are reported in Chapter 10.
Passenger cars are registered in combination with jeeps and taxis.
Before we proceed with calculations relating the number of vehicles in
use to sales, we first present demand equations for jeeps.

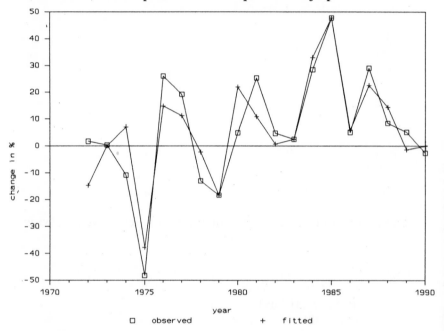

Figure 8.6: Sales of passenger cars: observed and fitted

Production and sale of jeeps, numerically of moderate importance
compared to commercial vehicles and passenger cars, grew constantly
since 1976 with an average annual growth rate of around 14%, compared
to around 5% in the period before 1976. Estimations of regression
equations for demand for jeeps generated the following result:

$$dls_{je,pc} = 4.58 - .46 * dlrp_{je} - .69 \, (ls_{je,pc,t-1} - 4.58 - 1.69 * lgdppc_{t-1})$$
$$(10.0) \quad (2.5) \qquad (5.7) \qquad\qquad (4.9) \quad (4.4)$$
$$-.19 * d76 + .17 * d80 - .14 * d85$$
$$(2.3) \qquad (2.1) \qquad (1.8)$$

R2 = .80; 16 observations; 1974-1989; (absolute) t-values in parentheses

where $s_{je,pc}$ =   per capita sales of jeeps
          rp_{je} =   price of jeeps deflated with cpi
          gdppc   =   per capita gross domestic product in constant
                          prices (1980=100)

(variables are transformed in first differences of logs: a 'd' before a variable-name stands for a first difference and an 'l' for natural log).

Some help of dummies (1976, 1980 and 1985) is required to realise an acceptable estimation result. The price elasticity is -.46, while the per capita income elasticity has a value of 1.69. We are unable to find a significant impact of nominal lending rates. A fitted equation has been plotted together with observations (see Figure 8.7). Again, forecasts for the period 1990-2020 are reported in Chapter 10.

Number of passenger cars in use

In line with the treatment of commercial vehicles the number of passenger cars (including jeeps) in use is derived from the sales of vehicles combined with the use of the vintage approach. The same

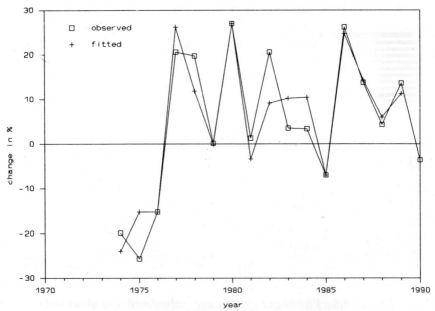

Figure 8.7: Sales of jeeps: observed and fitted

assumptions apply as in the case of commercial vehicles with respect to the general framework, only the numerical values differ. In case of passenger cars an average length of life is assumed to start at a level of 20 years in 1950 and to move slowly upwards over time to reach a value of 28 years in 1990. The oil-crises do have an impact on sales. However, this impact did not generate satisfactory results with respect to the calculated number of vehicles in use. Therefore an intensified discarding is assumed both in 1973 and 1975 reflecting the increased user cost of capital. Again the number of registrations has been lifted upward somewhat over the entire period by a constant number to allow for passenger cars for military purposes that do appear in sales figures but are not registered (Motor Vehicles Act, 1988, section 60). Figure 8.8 shows the calculated number of passenger cars in use as well as the registered number of passenger cars. Unfortunately the calculated figure is slightly lower than the observed one over the entire period. Imports of passenger cars or conceptual differences between sales and registrations probably will be the cause of this disappointing result. In Figure 8.9 the vintage composition in 1990 of passenger cars is presented.

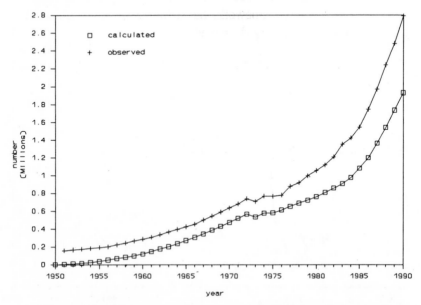

Figure 8.8: Passenger cars in use (calculated and observed)

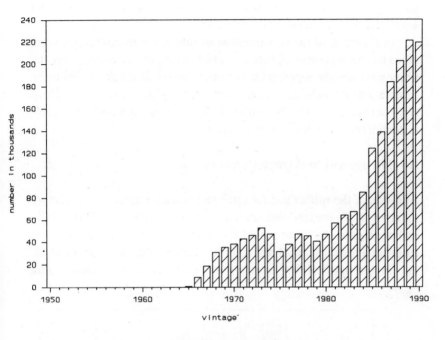

**Figure 8.9 : Calculated vintage composition of
passenger cars in 1990.**

Weight, tyre distance, driving and number of tyres

In order to calculate the consumption of rubber for replacement demand
of tyres, the same relationships apply as in the case of commercial
vehicles. However, there are less uncertainties with respect to the
average rubber weight per tyre and the average number of tyres per
vehicle mainly due to greater homogeneity in this group of vehicles.
Average tyre weight (i.e. gross use of rubber required to produce a
passenger vehicle tyre) is assumed to be 4.9 kg. for a regular tyre and 3.2
for a tyre for a Maruti type of car. The average number of tyres per
vehicle is fixed at 5:4 wheels plus a spare tire. Average tyre distance is
gradually rising over time, starting at 25000 km. in 1960 to 36000 km.
in 1990. This gradual rise of the average tyre distance becomes somewhat
stronger recently due to radialisation. Average driving distance for

passenger cars is assumed to be 10000 km per vehicle per year, and somewhat lower after the oil-crises.

In Figure 8.10 the consumption of rubber for motorcar tyres and tubes has been presented, both observed as well as calculated using the framework and the necessary assumptions as explained above. From the calculations it can be derived that in the case of passenger car and jeep tyres between 70 and 80% concerns replacements demand. This share is declining somewhat in recent times.

8.6 The agricultural tractor market

Analysis of the rubber use for tyres and tubes for agricultural tractors together with trailers and animal drawn vehicles is substantially complicated by, on the one hand, the enormous difference in rubber use for front and rear tyres of agricultural tractors, and, on the other hand, the limited applicability of our framework for tractors, trailers and

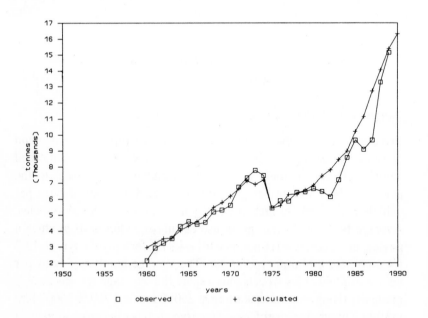

**Figure 8.10: Consumption of rubber for passenger
car tyres and tubes**

animal drawn vehicles. An effort to apply our framework to trailers and animal drawn vehicles fails altogether because of the lack of data (both of sales as well as registrations). Our framework is therefore slightly adjusted as will be explained below.

Demand equations for agricultural tractors have been estimated along the same lines as in the case of commercial vehicles. As series on prices are not available and therefore no estimates of price-elasticity are possible. Nominal lending rates contribute significantly to the explanation. With some effort we succeeded in generating a significant income-elasticity of 1.42. Dummies required to get a reasonable fit can be explained by the supply constraints created by the government: especially during the period 1982 to 1987 this policy had a negative impact on growth rates. A graph has been plotted with observed and fitted values (see Figure 8.11). Again forecasts are reported in Chapter 10.

$$dls_{at,pc} = 2.45 - 5.37 * dnlr_{t-1} - .31 * (ls_{at,pc,t-1} - 2.45 - 1.42 * lgdppc_{t-1})$$
$$(4.4) \quad (3.3) \qquad (6.8) \qquad\qquad (4.4) \quad (7.9)$$
$$-.17 * d85 - .21 * d86 - .42 * d87$$
$$(1.7) \qquad (2.1) \qquad (4.1)$$

R2 = .79; 27 observations; 1964-1990; (absolute) t-values in parentheses

where $s_{at,pc}$ =   per capita sales of agricultural tractors
        nlr   =   nominal lending rate
        gdppc   =   per capita gross domestic product in constant
                    prices (1980=100)

(variables are transformed in first differences of logs: a 'd' before a variable-name stands for a first difference and an 'l' for natural log)

Number of agricultural tractors in use

In line with our approach on commercial vehicles we continue with deriving the number of agricultural tractors in use from the sales of agricultural tractors and applying our vintage device. Only fragmentary data are available on the number of registered agricultural tractors. A time-series has been created by fitting a second degree polynomial of a time trend on the few observations that are available, and use the fitted equation as the series for 'registered agricultural tractors'. The average length of life of agricultural tractors turns out to be 17 years and is

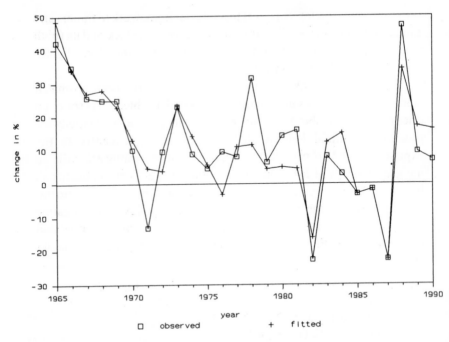

Figure 8.11: Sales of agricultural tractors: observed and fitted

assumed to be constant over time. Figure 8.12 shows the calculated and 'observed' number of agricultural tractors in use. The vintage model generates the created 'registrations' reasonably well from 1980 onwards.

Weight, tyre distance, driving distance and number of tyres

With agricultural tractors the extra information required to arrive at rubber consumption does not translate easily into variables like the average weight of tyres, average number of tyres, average tyre distance and average driving distance. First of all there is a huge difference in the rubber requirement of front and rear tyres. Next, the wear and tear of agricultural tractors and tyres for agricultural tractors, and thus their replacement, is not so much measured with the driving distance and tyre distance, but is much more related to the kind of use and the use intensity which are relatively hard to measure. Finally, our series for rubber

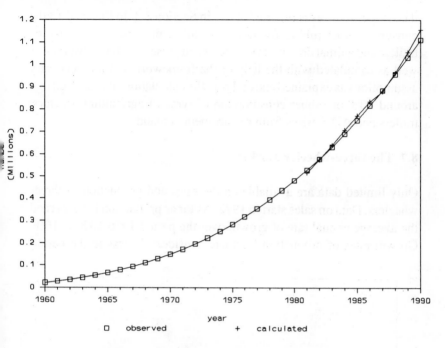

**Figure 8.12: Agricultural tractors in use:
calculated and observed**

consumption for agricultural tyres and tubes also includes tyres and tubes for trailers and animal drawn vehicles (ADV). The following simplifying assumptions are made to deal with these issues. Instead of specifying a far-fetched average driving distance and average tyre distance we postulate a simple replacement factor. This factor indicates the annual share of the number of vehicles in use of which the tyres are replaced. Rear tyres of agricultural tractors are hardly replaced. It is assumed that on an annual basis only 3-5% of the number of agricultural tractors in use have their rear tyres replaced. Front tyres of agricultural tractors are replaced every 2.5 years. In the calculations we have adjusted the number and the gross use of rubber of front tyres upward to allow for the existence of trailer tyres and tubes. The tyres for animal drawn vehicles is separately taken care of by assuming a trend development in tyre and tube production. The gross use of rubber for these types of tyres is reported above in Section 8.3. In Figure 8.13 the consumption of rubber for tyres and tubes of agricultural tractors, trailers and animal drawn vehicles has been presented, both observed as well as calculated with the help of the framework and the necessary assumptions as explained above. From the calculations it is derived that around 40% of rubber consumption of tyres of agricultural tractors, trailers and ADV arises from replacement demand.

8.7 The three-wheeler market

Only limited data are available on the sales and production of three-wheelers. Data on sales start in 1972. As far as production is concerned the average annual rate of growth over the period 1956-1990 is 16%. Growth rates of production fluctuate considerably less in the period

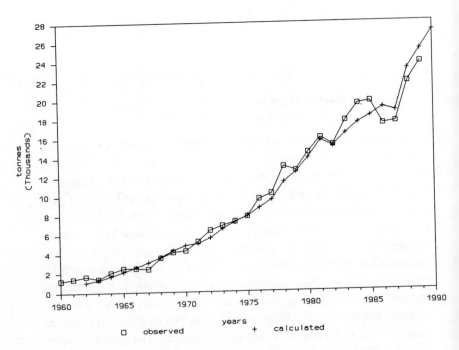

Figure 8.13: Consumption of rubber for tyres and tubes of tractors, trailers and ADV

from 1980 to 1990. Time-series on sales are extended backward with the help of the series on production. Estimations are run with all the standard variables, cq. per capita GDP, prices of three-wheelers relative to consumer prices, and both nominal and real lending rates. The following estimation result gives an adequate explanation of sales:

$$dls_{3w,pc} = 6.14 - .85 * dlrp_{3w} - .73 * (ls_{3w,pc,t-1} -6.14 - 2.01 * lgdppc_{t-1})$$
$$(8.4) \quad (2.3) \qquad (7.7) \qquad\qquad (8.4) \quad (17.8)$$
$$-.40 * d70 + .44 * d76$$
$$(3.0) \qquad (3.1)$$

$R2 = .78$; 23 observations; 1967-1989; (absolute) t-values in parentheses

where

$s_{3w,pc}$	=	per capita sales of 3-wheelers
rp_{3w}	=	price of 3-wheelers deflated with cpi
nlr	=	nominal lending rate
gdppc	=	per capita gross domestic product in constant prices (1980=100)

(variables are transformed in first differences of logs: 'd' before a variable-name stands for a first difference and an 'l' for natural log)

The price elasticity is −.85, while the per capita income elasticity has a value of 2.01. We are unable to find a significant impact of nominal lending rates. Observed and fitted values of per capita sales of three-wheelers are shown in Figure 8.14.

Number of three-wheelers in use

We continue with constructing the number of three-wheelers in use from the sales of three-wheelers and using our vintage framework. As data on the registration of three-wheelers is fragmentary, we apply the same procedure as in the case of agricultural tractors to create a series on registrations of three-wheelers. The average length of life of three-wheelers turns out to be 15 years and is assumed to be constant over time. Figure 8.15 shows the calculated number of three-wheelers in use as well as the registered number of three-wheelers.

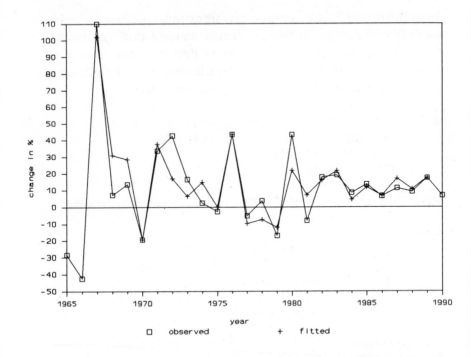

Figure 8.14: Sales of three-wheelers: observed and fitted

Weight, tyre distance, driving distance and number of tyres

Tyres and tubes of three-wheelers are technically very much like scooter tyres and tubes. In terms of rubber consumption for tyres and tubes, tyres and tubes for three-wheelers are taken together with tyres and tubes of scooters, motorcycles and mopeds. Therefore we deal with tyre weight, tyre distance, driving distance and number of tyres per three-wheeler in the section of two-wheelers.

8.8 The two-wheeler market

Demand equations produce unacceptable results if estimated for scooters, motorcycles and mopeds separately, possibly due to substantial substitution between respective types of two-wheelers. Estimating a demand equation on the aggregate level generates meagre results. We

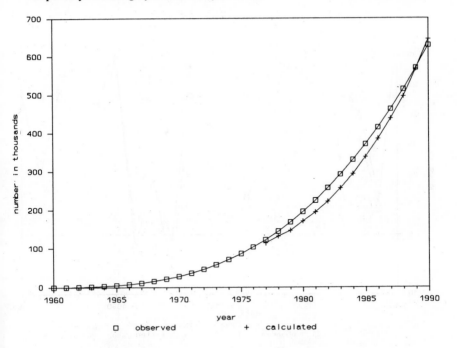

Figure 8.15: Three-wheelers in use: calculated and observed

were unable to detect a significant impact of prices of two-wheelers relative to consumer prices, both nominal and real lending rates and relative petrol prices. Nevertheless, a significant and high income elasticity was revealed. In Figure 8.16 realised and fitted growth rates of sales of two-wheelers are presented.

$$dls_{2w,pc} = 3.94 - .22 * (ls_{2w,pc,t-1} - 3.94 - 2.41 * lgdppc_{t-1})$$
$$(3.2) \ (2.6) \qquad\qquad (3.2) \ (14.6)$$
$$-.18 * d77 - .15 * d79$$
$$(2.7) \qquad (2.3)$$

R2 = .46; 23 observations; 1967-1989; (absolute) t-values in parentheses

where

$s_{2w,pc}$ = per capita sales of 2-wheelers

gdppc = per capita gross domestic product in constant prices (1980=100)

(variables are transformed in first differences of logs: a 'd' before a variable-name stands for a first difference and an 'l' for natural log)

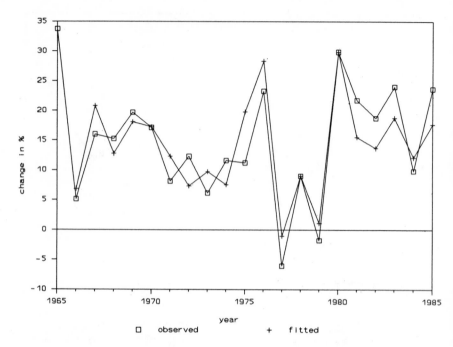

Figure 8.16: Sales of two-wheelers; observed and fitted

Number of two-wheelers in use and other variables

We proceed with constructing the number of two-wheelers in use from the sales of two-wheelers and by means of our vintage approach. Registration of two-wheelers does not distinguish scooters, motorcycles and mopeds. These types of two-wheelers, however, do have a different scrappage rate and length of life. Consequently, the vintage framework is built for these types of two-wheelers separately and then the number of two-wheelers in use is calculated by aggregating over types and compared with the (observed) registered number of two-wheelers. The average length of life of scooters, motorcycles and mopeds is 10, 10 and 8 years respectively and is assumed to be constant over time. Figure 8.17 shows the calculated number of two-wheelers in use as well as the registered number of two-wheelers.

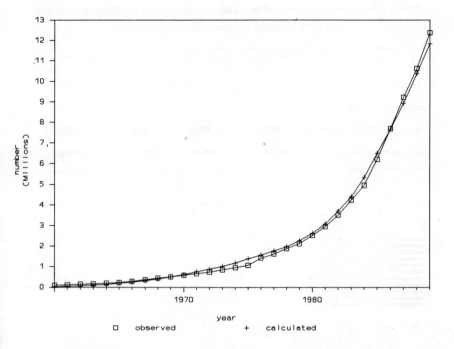

Figure 8.17: Two-wheelers in use: calculated and observed

As mentioned before, the consumption of rubber for two- and three-wheelers is taken together. Therefore, in order to take the step to calculate this category of rubber consumption, the results of the section on three-wheelers is combined with the results of this section. The additional assumptions with respect to the average weight of two-wheeler tyres, average number of tyres, average tyre distance and average driving distance are summarised in Table 8.5. In Figure 8.18 the observed and the calculated consumption of rubber for two- and three-wheeler tyres and tubes is plotted.

8.9 The bicycle market

The share of rubber consumption for bicycle tyres and tubes has been between 12% and 14.5% in the period 1965-1989. In 1989 this share was 14.3%, and thus of considerable importance for the rubber market (see

Table 8.5: Average gross rubber use, number of tyres, driving distance and tyre distance of two and three-wheelers

	scooters	motorcycles	mopeds	3-wheelers
Average gross rubber use	2.1	2.5	2.0	2.4
Average number of tyres	3	2	2	4
Average driving distance	5000	8000	3000	9000
Average tyre distance	40000	40000	30000	40000

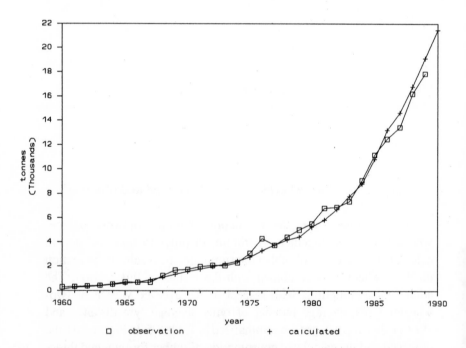

Figure 8.18: Consumption of rubber for tyres and tubes of two and three-wheelers

Figure 8.3). Series on sales of bicycles are altogether lacking. With reference to production and sales of other vehicles we assume sales to be equal to production. Demand equations are estimated with per capita

GDP, relative prices and nominal and real lending rates. The following equation more or less captures the fluctuations in 'sales' of the bicycles:

$$dlq_{bi,pc} = .34 - .67 * dlrp_{bi} - .35 * (lq_{bi,pc,t-1} - .34 - .71 * lgdppc_{t-1})$$
$$\quad\quad (.6)\ (1.8)\quad\quad (2.1)\quad\quad\quad (.6)\ (3.3)$$

$$\quad\quad -.20 * d75 + .12 * d78$$
$$\quad\quad (2.5)\quad\quad (1.7)$$

R2 = .58; 16 observations; 1972-1987; (absolute) t-values in parentheses

where $q_{bi,pc}$ =   per capita production of bicycles
          rp_{bi} =   price of bicycles deflated with cpi
          nlr   =   nominal lending rate
          gdppc   =   per capita gross domestic product in constant prices (1980=100)

(variables are transformed in first differences of logs: a 'd' before a variable-name stands for a first difference and an 'l' for natural log)

Due to doubtful estimation results, the sample period is truncated. The income elasticity is less than 1, namely .71, while the price-elasticity is -.67. In Figure 8.19 the observed and the fitted 'sales' of bicycles are shown.

In case of bicycles we also apply our framework with some slight modifications. These modifications are necessary because bicycles are not registered and there is little information on average tyre distance of bicycle tyres, and even less on average driving distance. As in the case of agricultural tractors average tyre distance and average driving distance hardly matter in the case of bicycles. The following adjustments have been made in our framework. A replacement factor for bicycle tyres and tubes is introduced along the same lines as in the case of agricultural tractors. This factor indicates the number of times per year the average bicycle tyre and tube has to be replaced. The lack of data on registration of bicycle makes it impossible to check our estimate of the number of bicycles in use. Data on the consumption of the rubber for bicycle tyres and tubes, however, are available directly from the Indian Rubber Statistics (we do not have to create these series on the basis of an aggregate, as in the case of all other types of vehicles) and presumably is of a better quality than the created series. Consequently we carry on,

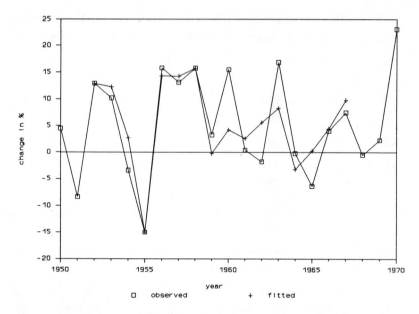

Figure 8.19: Sales of bicycles: observed and fitted

after creating a variable of the bicycles in use with the help of our vintage framework, for calculating the rubber consumption for bicycle tyres and tubes, and compare it with observations. The following assumptions have been made. The average gross use of rubber in producing a bicycle tyre is .496 kg. and for a tube .154 kg. The average length of life of a bicycle is assumed to be around 9.5 years. Bicycle tyres and tubes are assumed to last 1 to 2 years, and, thus, the replacement factor will be in between .5 and 1. In Figure 8.20 the observed and calculated consumption of rubber for bicycle tyres and tubes is presented.

8.10 Retreading

The demand for retreading material is, of course dependent on the demand for retreading worn out tyres, and this is in its turn depends on the tyre (retreading) distance,[10] the driving distance, the number of tyres per vehicle and the number of vehicles in use. The first two factors determine the frequency of retreading. At the beginning of this chapter

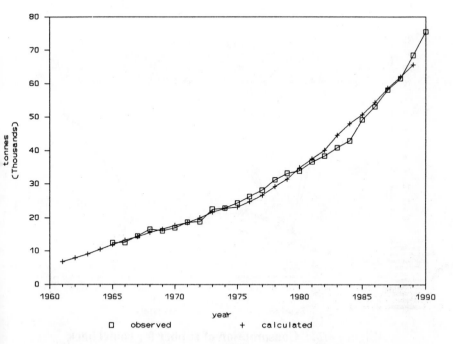

Figure 8.20: **Consumption of rubber for tyres and tubes of bicycles**

a relationship was set out that qualifies for empirical testing. We only have some scarce data on the retreading rate and on the amount of rubber used for retreading a tyre of a specific type. This adds to the difficulties, dealt with earlier, in the case of commercial vehicles to arrive at reasonable estimates of the average number of tyres per vehicle. To overcome these difficulties we prefer to estimate a simple relationship between the consumption of rubber for camel back and the number of vehicles in use by type, or

$$C_{retreading} = \sum \alpha_k \, viu_k$$

From equation (8.9) it follows that is the product of the retreading rate, rubber weight of retreading material per retreaded tyre, and the number of tyres per vehicle. Implicitly it is assumed that these variables are approximately constant over time for every type of vehicle. The number of different types of vehicles in use such as passenger cars,

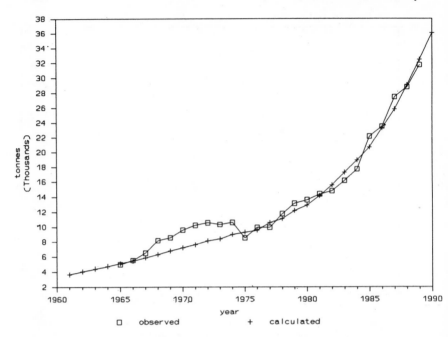

Figure 8.21: Consumption of rubber for camel back

commercial vehicles and two and three-wheelers are used in estimations. However, not surprisingly, enormous problems of multi-collinearity arise. Instead of carrying on along the path of estimation we have calculated the consumption of rubber for camel back, with a trial and error procedure on the values of k. Acceptable results are realised if we choose $\alpha_{cv}= 12.5$, $\alpha_{pc} = 4$ and $\alpha_{2w} = 0.25$. Figure 8.21 shows observed and calculated consumption of rubber for camel back.

8.11 Non-tyre rubber demand

A miscellaneous category of manufactured rubber products remains to be explained. In particular, this concerns seven categories of rubber consumption according to the end-product, namely: footwear; belts and hoses; latex foam and dipped goods; battery boxes; cables and wires and others. Because of the technical equality of latex foam and dipped goods, consumption of rubber for these products is taken together in the model. Consumption of rubber for the production of cables and wires and others is taken together as well, mainly because cables and wires is a quantitatively unimportant category (see also section 8.2). Some of the distinguished groups of manufactured rubber products are clearly consumer products (footwear), others are intermediate products used in industry (belts and hoses, cables and wires), or more specifically in the production of vehicles. Indeed, manufacturing of vehicles turns out to absorb a quite substantial extra amount of rubber on top of rubber consumption for tyres and tubes. Consumption of rubber for non-tyre purposes is strongly related with the production of vehicles. In our model, however, we apply a very simple approach in which per capita gross domestic product and relative price (if available) explain non-tyre consumption. Estimation results are summarised below.

$dlc_{fw,pc} = 1.05 - .11 * (lc_{fw,pc,t-1} - 1.05 - 1.47 * lgdppc_{t-1}) + .07\ d76 - .05\ d82 - .04\ d83$

$\qquad (6.2)\ (2.1) \qquad\qquad (6.2)\ (4.3) \qquad\qquad\qquad (3.5)\quad (2.5)\quad (2.2)$

$R2 = .74$; 20 observations; 1971-1990;

$dlc_{bh,pc} = 2.26 - .24 * dlrph - .76 * (lc_{bh,pc,t-1} - 2.26 - 1.01 * lgdppc_{t-1}) + .15\ d78 + .11\ d79$

$\qquad (7.7)\ (1.9) \qquad (5.9) \qquad\quad (7.7)\ (26.5) \qquad\qquad\quad (3.4) \qquad (2.4)$

$R2 = .71$; 18 observations; 1971-1988;

$dlc_{1fdg,pc} = 1.27 - 1.7 * (lc_{1fdg,pc,t-1} - 1.27 - 1.41 * lgdppc_{t-1}) - .16\ d74 - .23\ d75$

$\qquad (3.8)\ (2.8) \qquad\qquad (3.8)\ (9.4) \qquad\qquad\qquad (3.7) \qquad (4.9)$

$R2 = .60$; 25 observations; 1966-1990;

$dlc_{bb,pc} = 1.99 - .31 * dlrph - .70 * (lc_{bi,pc,t-1} - 1.99 - 1.10 * lgdppc_{t-1}) + .16\ d79$

$\qquad (5.3)\ (1.7) \qquad (3.3) \qquad\quad (5.3)\ (15.9) \qquad\qquad\qquad (2.5)$

$R2 = .46$; 18 observations; 1971-1988;

$dlc_{cwo,pc} = -.33 - .32 * (lc_{cwo,pc,t-1} + .33 - .22 * lgdppc_{t-1}) + .21\ d73 + .12\ d89$

$\qquad (.9)\quad (2.4) \qquad\qquad (.9)\ (1.7) \qquad\qquad\qquad (4.1) \qquad (2.2)$

$R2 = .64$; 24 observations; 1966-1989;

where

$c_{fw,pc}$	=	per capita consumption of footwear
rp_h	=	price of hoses deflated with cpi
$gdppc$	=	per capita gross domestic product in constant prices (1980=100)

and for suffix:

fw	=	footwear
bh	=	· belts and hoses
lfdg	=	latex foam and dipped goods
bb	=	battery boxes
cwo	=	cables and wires, and others

(variables are transformed in first differences of logs: a 'd' before a variable-name stands for a first difference and an 'l' for natural log; (absolute) t-values in parentheses)

8.12 Consumption of rubber by type

The final step that remains to estimate the share of NR in the total consumption of rubber by the end-product. Estimation results are summarised below. With some exceptions (footwear, cables and wires) all variables are transformed logarithmically. A few dummies are added to control for outliers. In Figures 8.27 and 8.28 the observed and the fitted shares are plotted.

$$l(c_{att,nr}/c_{att}) = 2.389 + .443\ l(c_{att,nr}/c_{att})_{t-1} - .033\ l(p_{nr}/p_{sr})_{t-1} + .032\ d78 - 0.21\ d89$$
$$\quad\quad\quad (3.5)\quad\quad (2.8)\quad\quad\quad\quad\quad (2.0)\quad\quad\quad\quad\quad (4.0)\quad\quad (2.5)$$

$R2 = .74$; 15 observations; sample period: 1976-1990

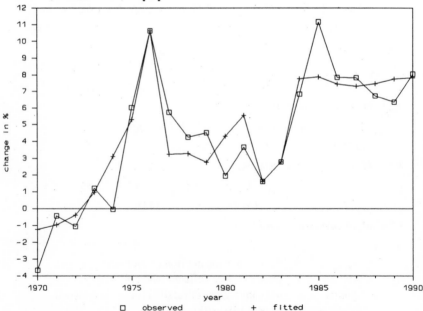

Figure 8.22: Consumption of rubber for footwear

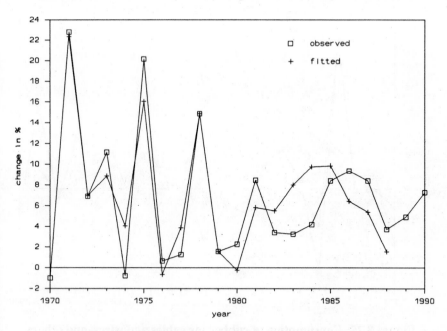

Figure 8.23: Consumption of rubber for belts and hoses

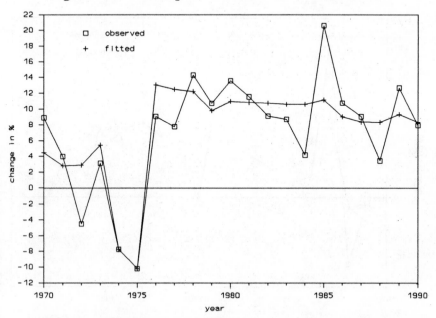

Figure 8.24: Consumption of rubber for latex foam and dipped goods

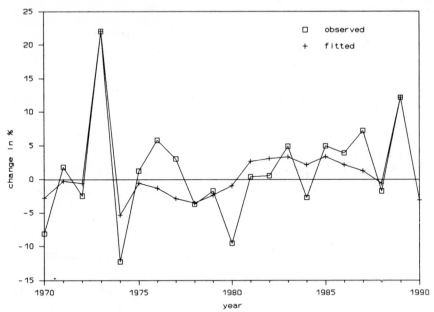

Figure 8.25: Consumption of rubber for cables and wires, and others

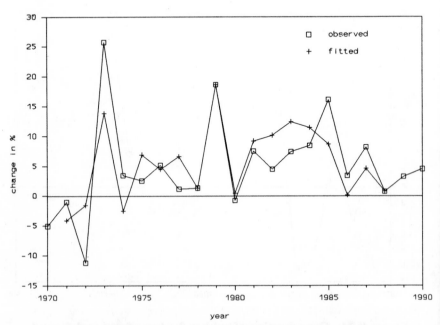

Figure 8.26: Consumption of rubber for battery boxes

$$l(c_{ctt,nr}/c_{ctt}) = 1.981 + .517 \, l(c_{ctt,nr}/c_{ctt})_{t-1} - .134 \, l \, (p_{nr}/p_{sr})_{t-1} + .025 \, d84\text{-}90$$
$$\quad\quad\quad (5.3)\quad\ (5.7)\quad\quad\quad\quad\quad (4.6)\quad\quad\quad\quad\quad (5.1)$$

$R2 = .96$; 14 observations; sample period: 1977-1990

Note: d84-90 is a dummy for the period 1984 to 1990 and takes the value 1 in these years and zero in other years

$$l(c_{cb,nr}/c_{cb}) = 1.521 + .639 \, l(c_{cb,nr}/c_{cb})_{t-1} - .277 \, l(p_{nr}/p_{sr})_{t-1} - 0.34 \, d81 + .066 \, d85$$
$$\quad\quad\quad (4.0)\quad\ (7.1)\quad\quad\quad\quad\quad (7.4)\quad\quad\quad\quad (2.3)\quad\quad\ (4.1)$$

$R2 = .96$; 12 observations; sample period: 1978-1989

$$l(c_{bb,nr}/c_{bb}) = 1.104 + .540 \, l(c_{bb,nr}/c_{bb})_{t-1} - .187 \, l(p_{nr}/p_{sr})_{t-1} + .192 \, d83$$
$$\quad\quad\quad (2.7)\quad\ (3.1)\quad\quad\quad\quad\quad (1.3)\quad\quad\quad\quad (2.6)$$

$R2 = .52$; 15 observations; sample period: 1976-1990

$$l(c_{bh,nr}/c_{bh}) = -.130 + 1.028 \, l(c_{bh,nr}/c_{bh})_{t-1} - .077 \, l \, (p_{nr}/p_{sr})_{t-1} - .027 \, d81 + .067 \, d86$$
$$\quad\quad\quad (.7)\quad\ (11.7)\quad\quad\quad\quad\quad (3.1)\quad\quad\quad\quad (2.0)\quad\quad\ (4.3)$$

$R2 = .91$; 15 observations; sample period: 1976-1990

$$c_{fw,nr}/c_{fw} = 74.2 - .634 \, TREND + 2.701 \, d79 - 1.945 \, d80$$
$$\quad\quad\quad (71.2)(8.9)\quad\quad\quad\ (2.5)\quad\quad\ (1.8)$$

$R2 = .91$; $DW = 2.0$; 14 observations; sample period: 1977-1990

$$c_{cw,nr}/c_{cw} = 74.3 - 1.655 \, TREND + 9.190 \, d77 - 5.268 \, d79 - 4.630 \, d84$$
$$\quad\quad\quad (61.2)\ (20.3)\quad\quad\quad\ (7.5)\quad\quad\ (4.6)\quad\quad\ (4.4)$$

$R2 = .99$; $DW = 1.8$; 14 observations; sample period: 1977-1990

$$l(c_{oth,nr}/c_{oth}) = 4.221 - .256 \, l(p_{nr}/p_{sr})_{t-1} - .055 \, d85$$
$$\quad\quad\quad (57.4)\quad (5.0)\quad\quad\quad\quad (2.1)$$

$R2 = .72$; $DW = 2.0$; 14 observations; sample period: 1977-1990

Dependent variable: share of NR in rubber consumption (c..,nr) in total rubber consumption (c..) by the end-product. Most variables are transformed logarithmically: an 'l' before a variable-name stands for the natural logarithm of that variable. A dummy for year xx is indicated with dxx and takes the value 1 in year xx and zero in other years. Explanation of subscripts: att = automotive tyres and tubes; ctt = cycle tyres and tubes; cb = camel back; bh = belts and hoses; bb = battery boxes; cw = cables and wires; fw. = footwear; oth = other end-products.

t-statistics are presented in brackets under the coefficients; DW = Durbin-Watson statistic; R2 = coefficient of correlation adjusted for degrees of freedom.

Estimation results are reasonable except for two exceptions: in the case of footwear, and cables and wires we did not succeed in finding an equation with a significant price impact. Probably the impact of price of NR relative to SR is non-existent in the manufacturing of these products. An ordinary specification with only a constant term and a trend variable as explanatory variables, however, proved to be very satisfactory, with coefficients of correlation as high as .99. Given the low significance of the price term in the equation for battery boxes, this impact is questionable in that case as well, which is not altogether strange. Battery boxes have

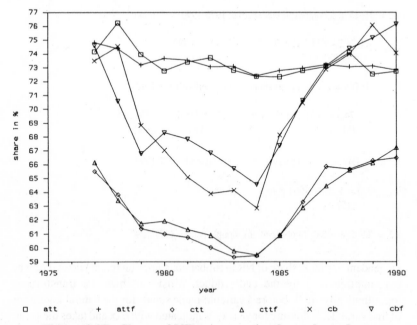

Figure 8.27: Share of NR consumption by end-product

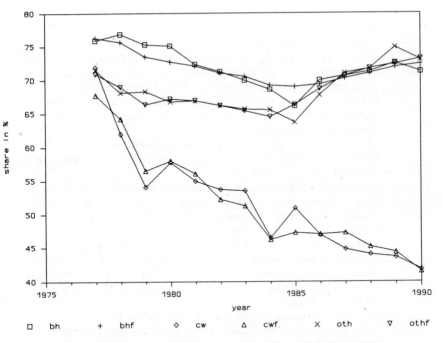

Figure 8.28: Share of NR consumption by end-product

a high content of reclaimed rubber: they do not react at all to fluctuations in the prices of natural rubber relative to the price of SR. Elasticities with respect to the price of NR relative to SR range from -.277 (consumption of rubber for camel back) to -.033 (consumption of rubber for automotive tyres and tubes).

The consumption of natural rubber aggregated over end-products will be referred to as consumption. In formula we have

$$c =' c_{nr} = \Sigma c_{i,nr}$$

This will be taken up in Chapter 10.

NOTES

1   Exports of tyres and tubes, and in general exports of manufactured rubber goods, gained in importance in the early nineties, and most likely will become more important in the future. These exports concern mainly bus and truck tyres (see

'Elastomer Demand Projections in Respect of Tyre Industry', ATMA, November 1991).

2   A bar above a variable indicates an average.

3   A visit to a tyre factory revealed that moderate switching to another mix of NR and SR is technically feasible and relatively easy to execute: No major adjustments in machinery are required. This makes us believe that the choice between NR and SR in consumption of rubber is to a considerable extent short run in character. Nevertheless, the share of NR used in tyres produced in this factory fluctuates over years as well.

4   The dependent variable actually is the consumption of natural rubber devided by the consumption of synthetic, natural and reclaimed rubber taken together, or in formula: $C_{NR}/(C_{NR} + C_{SR} + C_{RR})$.

5   Gross rubber weight per tyre is based on 'Elastomer Demand Projections in Respect of Tyre Industry', Automotive Tyre Manufactures Association (ATMA), November 1991. As the variance of the gross rubber weight per tyre, both in between and within countries, is much larger for tyres of commercial vehicles and two-wheelers (see Smit, 1982, pp. 138-140) some adjustments in the gross use of rubber per tyre have been made to achieve a good fit of the (sum of the) disaggregated series to the aggregate. In particular the sum of squared residuals of observed and calculated rubber consumption for automobile tyres and tubes has been minimised.

6   See *Rubber & Plastics News*, August 17, 1992, pp. 43-44.

7   In line with Chapter 6 latex foam and dipped goods are taken together. Cables and wires and other rubber end-products, however, are treated as one separate group in the share analysis.

8   Estimation of the share of NR in latex foam and dipped goods is therefore omitted.

9   In particular SBR-1502, SBR-1712, SBR-1958, PB, and others.

10   In the case of retreading we mean by average tyre distance the average number of kilometers that is required for a tyre to be worn out, but still of sufficient by good quality to be retreaded. It differs from our earlier concept of average tyre distance which refers to the number of kilometers that is required for a tyre to be totally worn out.

Part IV
Matching Natural Rubber
Supply and Demand:
Past and Future

9

THE DOMESTIC RUBBER MARKET
IN INDIA

9.1 Introduction

In this part we elaborate on the mechanism that matches supply and demand of natural rubber in India. First, a short verbal description of the mechanisms at work in the Indian natural rubber market as well as the institutional setting is presented (Chapter 9). Subsequently the modelling approach will be set out. Two separate models are elaborated: the first, set out in Chapter 10, is a model with annual data, and is particularly suitable to make long run forecasts or long run simulations. The model connects the production of rubber as formalised in Chapter 6 and consumption of rubber as formalised in Chapter 8. Projections for various scenarios are presented as .well.

9.2 The Indian rubber economy and the world-market

The domestic Indian price of NR has been generally higher than the international price. In 1956 the government of India had ordered that the manufacturers should pay to the Rubber Board the difference between the price of imported rubber and indigenous natural rubber so that manufacturers would get natural rubber at the same cost in India, irrespective of the source of supply, and also to prevent the tendency of manufacturers going in for imported natural rubber. This was in accordance with the policy of price protection given to the NR industry. This system of payments of the price differential of imported and indigenous rubber by manufacturers to the Rubber Board, continued up to the close of the 1960s. In 1957, the government also introduced an import duty on natural rubber in line with the general import policy. Initially the duty was 5% which was enhanced to 10% in March 1961 and again to 22% in April 1963. In February 1965 the duty was further enhanced to 32% which included a regulatory duty of 10%.

During the 1950s and 1960s manufacturers of rubber goods were allowed to import rubber directly to the extent indicated by the licences issued to them. However, this was found to be not very effective due to various reasons such as the difficulty in estimating the actual gap in advance, variations in the international price, untimely import by manufacturers etc. Consequently at the end of 1968 the State Trading Corporation of India Ltd. (STC), a public sector undertaking under the Government of India was brought into the natural rubber field for importing natural rubber and regulating supplies so that the gap between indigenous supply and demand could be bridged and so that local producers were not adversely affected. Initially, STC functioned more or less as an advisory body for monitoring and regulating imports. During the period from 1970-71 to 1977-78, the STC had to enter the domestic market and carry out price support operations as a fall in the demand during the period had resulted in a fall in prices to an uneconomic level. These operations also included export of small quantities as domestic supply during the period was in excess of the demand, mainly as a result of the slackening of demand caused by the energy crises. The country became a net importer from 1978-79 onwards (see Figure 9.1) and STC has been authorised to import and distribute natural rubber to actual users. STC used to import and distribute natural rubber during the lean production season when domestic production would be less than consumption and the market price showed a run-away tendency.

The purpose of this chapter is to get a better picture as to how supply comes to match the demand (or *vice versa*), both internally and externally. What happens if consumption of rubber exceeds or falls short of production? Unlike the text-book situation of perfectly competitive domestic and world markets,[1] India can be considered an almost closed economy. We will put forward some empirical facts to substantiate the proposition that the Indian rubber market is sufficiently isolated from the world market to rule out any impact of the world market.

In Figures 9.2 and 9.3 the development of the domestic price of RMA4[2] is presented together with the world-market price of RSS[3] (Singapore), and synthetic rubber, both including and excluding import

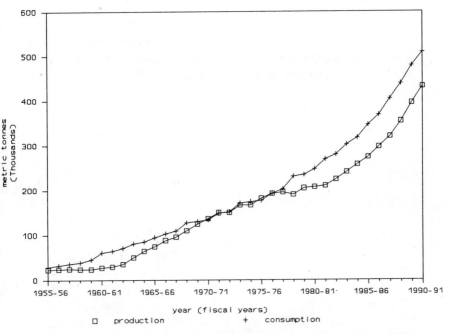

Figure 9.1: **Total consumption and production of natural rubber**

duties. From these figures it is clear that during the larger part of the last 25 years, the domestic price of natural rubber is higher than, or at least as high as, the world-market price. The difference between the world-market prices and the domestic prices is more than offset by import duties. Usually the price plus import duty is much higher than the domestic price. Only in some periods the import price of rubber has been more or less equal to the domestic to price. Also, fluctuations in the world market price seem to have little correspondence with the price of NR and SR in the domestic market. As mentioned above the STC is engaged in importing rubber and its distribution among manufacturers of rubber products from 1978. In addition, manufacturers exporting rubber products are also allowed to import rubber directly without duty to the extent it would be used for manufacturing the products exported, thus enabling them to compete in the international market. This incentive was in operation from the beginning of the 1960s. For the benefit of the small scale manufacturers who would find it difficult to import rubber,

the difference between the Indian and the international price has been
subsidised by the Rubber Board from 1975. However, up to 1988 only
a relatively negligible share of imports, compared to imports by the
STC, has been effected by manufacturers.

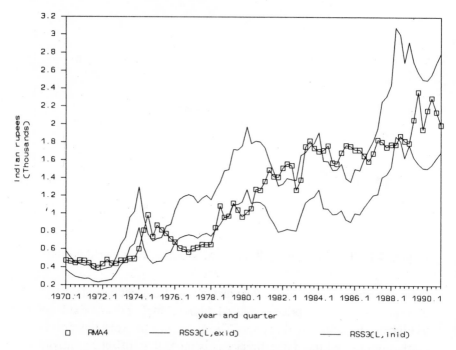

**Figure 9.2: Domestic (RMA4) and world-market price (RSS3)
of natural rubber**

Releasing of imported natural rubber by the STC presumably
occurs whenever the price of natural rubber rises and the gap between
consumption and production becomes very big, and manufacturers of
rubber products experience shortages in buying inputs for their
production. In the case of maximum price the release of imported rubber
by the STC is also related to the price development. As soon as the price
hits the ceiling the STC intervenes in the market by releasing stocks of
rubber, if available. Finally all foreign transactions require a licence.
Especially at times of scarcity of foreign exchange this would create a
barrier to import.

We can conclude that high import duties, both for synthetic and natural rubber, import licensing, foreign exchange shortages, and the presence of the STC, have effectively isolated the Indian rubber economy from the world-market. The export promotion scheme is just a small step towards more transactions of the private sector directly with the world-market.

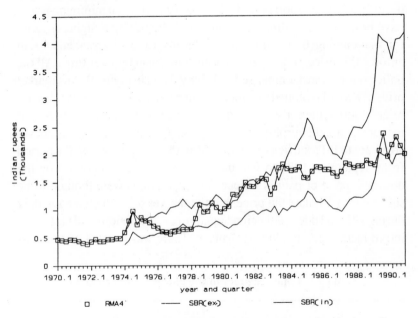

Figure 9.3: Domestic (RMA4) and world-market price of synthetic rubber (SBR)

Source: *Indian Rubber Statistics*, Rubber Board of India

9.3 Domestic price formation of natural rubber

Substantial fluctuations in natural rubber prices induced the government of India to take up a policy to stabilise these prices. The domestic price of natural rubber in India had been statutorily controlled by the government from May 1942 to September 1981 with a short break of about 15 months from October 1946. During the period from December 1947 to December 1963 and again from October 1967 to November 1968, maximum price had also been enforced. The prices thus fixed

were reviewed and revised from time to time taking into account the cost
of production, yield per hectare etc., so as to provide an incentive to
producers to expand and modernise cultivation and production of
natural rubber. The prevention of sharp decline in prices and thereby
provision of an income guarantee to small-holders and estates was also
an important goal. Indeed, maximum prices have been effective only
during a relatively short period (1986.02-1989.01), but minimum prices
have been effective almost continuously, suggesting a higher priority
for maintaining minimum prices. The institutional arrangements to
enforce this price protection has been some changes over time. All the
policy regimes are summarised in Table 9.1 and in Figure 9.4 the market
price of RMA4 is plotted together with notified maximum and minimum
prices. During the early 1970s, the depression period already discussed
in more detail, the surplus was too big and the infrastructure was not yet
adequate to lift a sufficient amount from the market. During the period
from September 1981 to February 1986 there was no control on the
domestic price of natural rubber. STC operations were thought to be
sufficient to regulate the price, but the market price fluctuated widely
during 1981-83 due to either inadequate or excess imports and variations
in production due to climate changes. There was conflict of opinions

Table 9.1: Policy regimes in the natural rubber market

Period from / to	Policy		
	minimum price	maximum price	other
1942.05 - 1946.09	yes	no	
1946.10 - 1947.11	-	-	
1947.12 - 1963.12	yes	yes	
1964.01 - 1967.09	yes	no	
1967.10 - 1968.11	yes	yes	
1968.12 -			entry of STC in the market
1968.12 - 1981.08	yes	no	
1981.09 - 1986.02	no	no	
1986.02 - 1988.09	yes	yes	BSS
1988.10 - 1991.01	yes	yes	BSS
1991.01 -	yes		

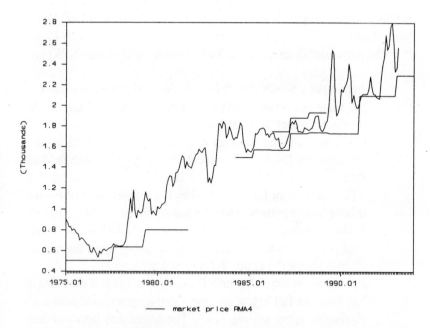

Figure 9.4: **Notified maximum and minimum price and market price of natural rubber (RMA4)**

among the rubber growers and rubber users about the demand-supply gap as well as the reasonable price of natural rubber. It was felt that it would no longer be possible to ensure stability in natural rubber prices based on release of natural rubber during lean production season alone.

In the period from April 1986 to March 1989 the Government, by means of the STC, made use of a Buffer Stocking Scheme (BSS) to intervene in the market. The policy aimed at stabilising the price of natural rubber at a level remunerative to rubber growers and fair to the producers of rubber products. The scheme comprised a minimum and a maximum price for RMA IV and RMA V grades of natural rubber. These minimum and maximum prices were calculated on the basis of studies on the costs of production and were revised every now and then.[3] The scheme is operated by the STC and the price in the market is regulated by releasing accumulating stocks when the price tends to go above the upper band and buying and accumulating stocks of natural rubber from the domestic market when the price tends to go below the lower band.

The particular features of the Buffer Stocking Scheme (BSS) are:

-    fixation of a Bench Mark Price (fair price) for natural rubber on the basis of cost of production and a reasonable return to the producers which is affordable to manufacturers;
-    the lower and upper trigger level prices are fixed with a difference of Rs. 300 per tonne with respect to the Bench Mark Price;
-    STC would enter the market when the market price of natural rubber (in particular the Market indicator price which is the 15/7-days moving average daily price) falls below the lower trigger level price and release natural rubber when the market price is above the upper trigger level price;
-    Market intervention by the STC should ensure that the price of NR does not fall below the lower ceiling price, nor does it go above the upper ceiling price. The lower and upper ceiling prices are fixed Rs. 500 per tonne below and above the Bench Mark Price.

Under the scheme, the Bench Mark Price, which was fixed at Rs. 16,500 per tonne for RMA4 grade in February 1986 was enhanced to Rs. 17,000 in May 1987, Rs. 17,800 in September 1988 and again to Rs. 21,450 in January 1991. In January 1993 the bench mark price was again revised to Rs. 23,450 for RMA IV and to Rs. 22,950 for RMA V grade. STC carried out procurement of natural rubber as price support during peak production seasons in 1986, 1988, 1991 and 1992 and released natural rubber to the user industry in all the years in lean production season to arrest the upward trend in price. Under the scheme, the buffer stock to be maintained at any time during the lean production season was 2500 tonnes, which was, to be drawn down at the beginning of peak production season. The top graph of Figure 9.5 is the same as Figure 9.4, but now focusing on the period in which the Buffer Stock Scheme was operational. Some inferences should be possible as to the working of this price support scheme. When the domestic market price touched the lower band stocks at the STC were increased and when the domestic market price touched the upper band stocks at the STC were released (and imports increased). The pressure to import presumably will become stronger the smaller the stocks of rubber in the economy and the larger the price difference between the domestic and the world-markets.

The interaction between prices and stock formation plays a crucial role in the mechanism that matches supply and demand in the natural rubber market in India. In general, changes in stocks arise due to fluctuations in production, government policy with respect to the price natural rubber and, finally, behaviour of manufacturers of rubber products to secure input of rubber. Production of natural rubber, which is between 70% and 80% of total rubber production in India, has a distinctive seasonal pattern. There are two lean periods, namely February/March and June/July, and two peak periods during the year, in particular the months May, and November to January of which the latter period without exception shows the highest production. Price support from the government creates an income guarantee for rubber producers in the short run. The huge short run supply fluctuations create substantial, and to some extent forced, stock formation in times of intensive tapping, and depletion of stocks with the growers and dealers in the slack season. In the long run price policies may have an impact on the investment in rubber trees, and hence on the production of rubber. The price support policy also has an impact on manufacturers of rubber products. In case a decline in price is effectively stopped by the STC, manufacturing industry buys the inputs more costly, compared to a situation without price protection. Increased cost levels might decrease profitability in this industry and thereby future investments. However, manufacturers of rubber products require a continuous stream of input of rubber to feed the production process. To avoid both the extremes, price rises as well as acute shortages, manufacturers of rubber products also follow a buying and stock formation policy. In case the market price of natural rubber is stabilised, manufacturers require less stocks to avoid these risks.

How do we formalise these observations into an empirical model of the Indian rubber market? The second section of the next chapter will be

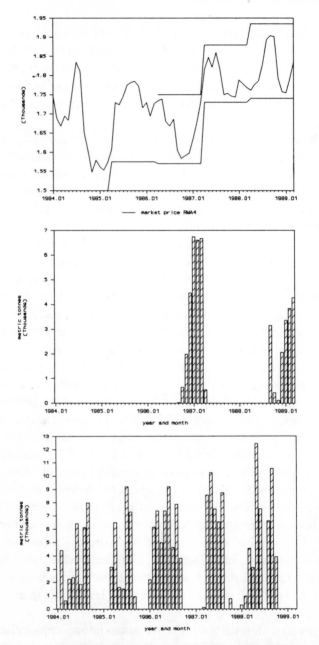

Figure 9.5: Domestic price of natural rubber (RMA4), procurement and releases by the State Trading Corporation during Buffer Stocking Scheme (BSS)

devoted to the specification of a formal model. Afterwards, in sections 10.3 and the following section, we will look at the future, reviewing what others have said and how this fits with our analysis.

NOTES·

1   In the case of perfectly competitive domestic and world-markets with fixed exchange rates, there will be one price for natural rubber, determined in the world-market. Temporary deviations of domestic and world-market prices might exist. Excess domestic demand, a situation prevailing in the Indian rubber economy during almost the entire period from 1955-1990, will create an upward pressure on the domestic price of rubber and on the utilisation rate in supply, stocks of rubber will be depleted, and, there will be a strong propensity to import rubber. If the domestic price increases relative to the price in the world-market it will be profitable for manufacturers of rubber products to buy their input in the world-market. Demand will shift towards the world-market, creating a downward pressure on domestic rubber prices. This pressure will continue until the domestic and the world-market prices are equal. If, for whatever reason, the price of rubber in the world-market is above the domestic price, it is much more profitable for manufacturers of rubber products to buy their inputs domestically. Suppliers of rubber, however, will be inclined to sell their production in the world-market. This will create a reduction of supply in the domestic market, and thus an upward pressure on the domestic price. To summarise, in a free market situation with fixed exchange rates, it is very unlikely that a price difference between the world-market and the domestic market will last for a very long time. If consumption of rubber falls short of production, an analogous (but opposite) chain of events will take place.

2   RMA4 and RSS3 refer to specific quality grades of natural rubber; RMA grades are only used in India; RSS originates from Malaysia and is a common quality denominator in the world market. RMA4 is equivalent to RSS3; SBR = Styrene Butadiene Rubber.

3   In some issues of the Indian Rubber Statistics summary statistics were presented on the 'Structure of Notified Price of RMA 1 Grade Rubber' in the past.

10

SUPPLY AND DEMAND :
INTERACTIONS AND PROJECTIONS

10.1 Introduction

In this chapter we analyze the demand for how natural rubber for disaggregated consumption categories (discussed in Chapters 7 and 8) is matched with production of natural rubber (discussed in Chapter 6). Connecting the model of total consumption of natural rubber with the model of total production of natural rubber requires that other components of supply, apart from the domestic production, and other components of demand apart from domestic consumption, are formalised. In section 10.2 a relatively simple procedure is presented to close the model. With the completed model we are in the position to construct scenarios for the future. In connection with the presentation of our projections we will offer a review on the applicability of selected perspectives on (parts of) the Indian Rubber Industry as delineated by committees and institutions. In section 10.4 synthetic rubber supply is briefly reviewed and in section 10.5 we present the case for future natural rubber supply including the ingredients for the various alternative scenarios. Finally, in section 10.6 the demand side is discussed and various scenarios are drawn. Also some combinations of alternative scenarios on the demand side and the supply side are constructed and the projection results are presented. It needs to be stressed that the number of scenarios is unlimited and that software and databanks are available with the authors to update the work and run new combinations. For this reason the current chapter has been kept relatively small.

10.2 Closing the model, liberalization and price projections

Closing the model

With the results of Chapters 6 and 8 we are in a position to complete the annual model. From Chapter 6 the production equation reads:

$$q = q_n$$

That is, production is assumed to be equal to normal production. Normal production, in its turn is determined by yield by age, age and vintage of the plantations (see Chapter 6). From Chapter 8 we have:

$$c = \sum c_{i,nr}$$

Consumption is the sum of consumption of natural rubber, specified by product. The two main consumer products distinguished are tyres and non-tyre products. The former is determined by the type of vehicle, the sales of vehicles, the vehicle population, prices of vehicles and some additional technical variables. The latter is determined by per capita GDP (see Chapter 8).

Stocks at growers and dealers (n_{gd}) and stocks at manufacturers (n_{mnf}) will in the long run be determined by consumption, due to some type of transaction demand. With respect to these stocks we assume a simple loglinear relationship connecting the level of stocks with consumption of NR, or:

$$n_{gd} = n_{gd}(c)$$
$$n_{mnf} = n_{mnf}(c)$$

Estimation results of these equations are:

$$l(n_{gd}) = -.5672 + .7522\, l(n_{gd,t-1}) + .2582\, l(c_{t-1})$$
$$\quad\quad (1.0) \quad (7.5) \quad\quad\quad (2.4)$$

$R2 = .93$; 38 observations; sample period: 1953-1990

$$l(n_{mnf}) = 1.5954 + .5654 \; l(n_{mnf,t-1}) + .2248 \; l \, (c_{t-1})$$
$$\quad (2.9) \quad\quad (4.6) \quad\quad\quad\quad (2.6)$$

$R2 = .86$; 38 observations; sample period: 1953-1990

Dependent variable: stocks of NR (n_{xx}); c = consumption of NR. Variables are transformed logarithmically: an 'I' before a variable-name stands for the natural logarithm of that variable. T-statistics are presented in brackets under the coefficients; DW = Durbin-Watson statistic; R2 = coefficient of correlation adjusted for degrees of freedom.

Finally, a price equation is added to the model. Assuming there is no liberalisation of trade, the price of natural rubber is assumed to depend on the last year's gap between production and consumption. The gap between supply and demand expresses the tension in the market: with relatively high supply a downward pressure on prices can be expected, and with a relatively high demand an upward pressure on prices can be expected.

$p = p[(q-c)_{t-j}]$ without trade liberalisation

The estimation result of this equation is:

$$dl(p) = -.0235 - .482 \; l[(q_{t-1} + .886 \; m_{t-1})/c_{t-1}]$$
$$\quad (.8) \quad\quad (1.5) \quad\quad\quad (3.4)$$

$R2 = .57$; 35 observations; sample period: 1956-1990

Dependent variable: price of NR (p) deflated with the general consumer price index; q = production of NR; m = imports of NR; c = consumption of NR. A 'd' before a variable-name stands for the first difference of that variable.

In the forecasts imports and exports are determined residually: whenever production (q) is higher than domestic consumption (c) and domestic stock formation $(\Delta n_{gd}, \Delta n_{mnf})$, the surplus will be exported, and, analogously, whenever production (q) is lower than domestic consumption (c) and domestic stock formation $(\Delta n_{gd}, \Delta n_{mnf})$ the gap will be met by imports. From the above outline of the model it is clear that both export and import have to be interpreted as net export and net import.

Liberalization and price projections

To assume complete isolation from the world market might not be a very appropriate assumption for the near future: indeed, the end of the eighties and the beginning of the nineties have witnessed some serious steps towards a more liberalised trade policy. In most of the scenarios an attempt is made to outline a situation of less isolation from the world market. Practically, this implies that the price formation is dictated by the world market, and by some policy variables, namely the exchange rate and the import duties on synthetic and natural rubber. In this situation the price equation as set out above is no longer valid. In fact, the applied price equation given trade liberalisation is:

$$p = p_{world} \text{ with trade liberalisation.}$$

In the remainder of this chapter both scenario-independent and scenario-dependent assumptions are highlighted and forecasts on consumption, production and price forecasts with these assumptions are presented.

The impact of a liberalised trade policy is felt in many areas. While there may be direct effects in terms of investment and production, the essential effect of opening-up comes through prices, which in our case are the price of natural rubber, the price of synthetic rubber, the consumer price index and the prices of vehicles. Indeed, as is explained before (see footnote 1, Chapter 9) prices in the world-market will, in the long run, dominate the domestic market entirely. In case of perfectly competitive domestic and world-markets and fixed exchange rates, there will be one price for natural rubber determined in the world-market. In less than perfectly competitive situations, domestic prices can only temporarily deviate from world market prices. In a free market situation with fixed exchange rates, it is very unlikely that a price difference between the world-market and the domestic market will last for a very long time.

An assessment in quantitative terms of the effects of opening up of the natural rubber sector of the Indian economy requires a model which is more elaborate in a number of areas than the model developed in the previous chapters. We refrain from assessing the impact of trade liberalisation on domestic consumption of the aggregate of all types of rubbers. We do not adjust any part of the model on the demand equations presented in Chapter 8. Similarly on the supply side, no impact is incorporated of a liberalised trade policy. As an example, we have kept the price of passenger cars as given (exogenous in terms of the model). It will be necessary to guess the influence of opening up on vehicle prices and impose it by assumption. Another example is that we have assumed imports and exports of rubber goods to remain negligible compared to domestic consumption. This will also have to be validated. However, although our model is not particularly equipped to simulate a fully liberalised market it is reasonably capable of showing the impact of liberalisation.

To formalise the impact of the opening up of the economy on the rubber market in an *adhoc* way we assume that the domestic prices of natural rubber and synthetic rubber gradually and exogenously move towards the world market price of natural rubber and synthetic rubber. Figure 10.1 shows the projection for the prices of both RMA4 and SBR/PB. The world market price of the comparable grade RSS3 in US is projected to remain at the 1992 level during 1993, to increase 10% in 1994 and another 5% in 1995, and to remain constant afterwards. The US$ dollar rupee-exchange rate jumped from Rp. 17.50 in 1990 to 22.80 in 1991, 29.50 in 1992, and 31.00 in 1993 and is assumed to increase by 0.5% annually afterwards. The import duty in 1992 was 70% and we have assumed it to decline gradually to 0 in about 5 years. Incorporating these elements and assuming complete liberalization in due course, gives the domestic price of NR based on the world market. In 1992 the import duty for SR was 110%. We have assumed a similar period for a decline to 0% as in the case of NR. As argued above, actual domestic prices will converge to a level dictated by the world market. A gradual process has been assumed during the second half of the 1990s for both NR and SR. Note that in the world market by assumption there is no average price difference between SR and RSS3.

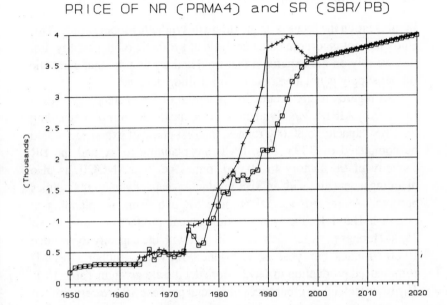

PRICE OF NR (PRMA4) and SR (SBR/PB)

**Figure 10.1: Projected price of NR (RMA4) and
SR (SBR/PB) with opening up**

At this stage we would like to emphasize that the values of forecasts should be taken as merely indicative: over a period of more than 25 years markets tend to change drastically, and in a way that is impossible to model.[1] The most important insights from this study are gained by comparing different scenarios. By incorporating a lot of influences that can be quantified, the framework developed in the preceding chapters allows us to quantify and evaluate several influences in the long run and under different circumstances. To keep the model uptodate it is required to adjust it to the new institutional and structural environment in the course of time.

10.3 Plans for and projections of synthetic rubber supply

In this section the focus is on the future of synthetic rubber supply. This study has not incorporated an analysis of synthetic rubber supply. For this we rely on the experts in that field and we assume that synthetic rubber supply is not a bottleneck in fulfilling demand.

As regards future production potential of SR, a steady growth is foreseen by AIRIA: M/s. Synthetics & Chemicals Ltd. are now expanding the SBR capacity to 80,000 tonnes; the first phase of expansion would be completed by 1993, M/s. IPCL are planning to expand the BR capacity of the factory to 50,000 tonnes per year. NOCIL is also planning a new unit with an SBR production capacity of 80,000 tonnes per year. As regards special purpose SR two firms are planning to establish Butyl Rubber plants with annual production capacity of 25,000 tonnes per year each. A small unit with the capacity to produce 10,000 tonnes per year of Ethylene Propylene Rubber (EPDM) commenced production in 1992. More details are given in Table 10.1. The requirements of other types of special purpose SR are very limited

Table 10.1: Estimated present and future capacity of SR

Company	Grade	Present (tonnes)	Future capacity by 2000 (tonnes)
1. Synthetics and Chemicals Ltd.	SBR	40,000	80,000
	NBR	2,000	7,500
2. Indian Petrochemicals Ltd.	BR	20,000	50,000
3. National Organic Chemical Industries Ltd. (new unit)	SBR	-	80,000
4. Apar (P) Ltd.	SBR	3,750	30,000
5. UB Group (new unit)	Butyl	-	25,000
6. Gujarath Apar Ltd.	NBR	6,250	6,250
7. Herdilia Monomers Ltd. (new unit)	EPDM	-	10,000
8. Polyolefine Industries Ltd. (new unit)	EPDM	-	10,000
9. Asian Paints	VP Latex	780	1,500
10. Other small units	VP Latex/Silicon	-	2,500
Total		73,000	303,000

Source: *Handbook of Rubber Statistics* AIRIA (January 1993)

and may be of the total order of 10,000 to 15,000 tonnes per year in the 1990s. It may not be economical to produce these grades domestically, so these have to be imported.

10.4 Planting programmes and supply projections for natural rubber

Official plans

A perspective plan has been prepared by the Rubber Board with a view to achieve self-sufficiency in NR. The following are the salient features of the scheme:

a) expand the area under rubber cultivation by 160,000 ha. by 2000 AD;

b) speed up the replantation of old and low yielding trees with modern high yielding cultivars; the target is to replant 84,000 ha. by 2000 AD (see Table 10.2);

c) raise the productivity of the existing areas by popularising discriminatory fertiliser applications based on soil and leaf analysis, systematic plant protection from diseases by spraying fungicides, efficient crop harvesting through improved tapping practices, rain guarding of rubber trees and chemical stimulation of yield in older trees; thrust will be given to group processing and marketing among smallholders.

The total investment proposed under the scheme is Rs. 6600 million during the VII Five-Year Plan period, comprising of Rs. 2100 million by the Rubber Board, Rs. 1280 million by the financial institutions and the balance by the beneficiaries. The implementation of the project would step up the production to 522,000 tonnes by 1995-96 and to 675,000 tonnes by AD 2000. The productivity during these years is projected as 1350 kg./ha. and 1525 kg./ha. respectively vide the VIII Five Year Plan for rubber. This will be taken up again in the following sections when alternative scenarios are designed.

In the VIII five-year plan for NR, prepared by the Rubber Board, one of the subjects is the NR availability from 1990 to 2000. Largely

Table 10.2: Targets of new planting and replanting (ha.)

	New Planting		Total	Replanting
	Traditional	Non-traditional		
1992-93	4,000	8,000	12,000	7,000
1993-94	3,500	10,500	14,000	8,000
1994-95	3,000	13,000	16,000	9,000
1995-96	2,500	15,500	18,000	10,000
1996-97	2,000	18,000	20,000	10,000
1997-98	2,000	18,000	20,000	10,000
1998-99	2,000	18,000	20,000	10,000
1999-00	2,000	18,000	20,000	10,000
2000-01	2,000	18,000	20,000	10,000

following the figures on planting as mentioned above and brought in by the Rubber Board, as well as assumptions on other parameters also discussed in our report, the draft report suggests projections as presented in Table 10.3

Table 10.3: Projected production of natural rubber

Year	Total Area ('000 ha.)	Tapped Area ('000 ha.)	Yield (kg./ha.)	Production ('000 tonnes)
1990-91 (actual)	451	306	1076	330
1991-92	461	325	1125	365
1992-93	473	342	1180	405
1993-94	487	358	1240	445
1994-95	503	373	1300	485
1995-96	521	387	1350	522
1996-97	541	398	1390	553
1997-98	561	407	1430	582
1998-99	581	416	1465	609
1999-2000	601	427	1495	638
2000-2001	621	443	1525	675

Source:Report by the Rubber Board (1989).

**Table 10.4: Data on planting and three new planting
scenarios for natural rubber**

	New planting			Total area		
	optimistic	pragmatic	conservative	optimistic	pragmatic	conservative
1990		15143			475083	
1995	18000	15000	12000	546671	540601	534601
2000	22000	17000	10000	652140	622106	584106
2005	25000	18000	10000	771663	708645	631646
2010	27000	19000	10000	901551	799542	678547

Planting scenarios for this study

Some assumptions are required to construct scenarios. With respect to production of natural rubber the assumptions are formulated as follows. The levels of new planting up to 2010 are as in Table 10.4 and Figure 10.2. Three scenarios have been distinguished: an optimistic scenario with new planting levels going up to 35,000 ha. per year, a *pragmatic scenario* with new planting reaching 21,000 ha. year and a *conservative scenario* with new planting going down to 10,000 ha. per year. The average age at the time of discarding has been kept constant to the latest figure, the level in 1991, in view of the results described in Chapter 6, arguing that the shift to the higher yielding clones (RRII-105 etc.) has been completed and that no advantage can be expected from earlier replanting. Besides, the trend during the last few years even showed an increase in the average age. The percentage of discarded area to be replanted with natural rubber has been kept at the 1991 level of 95% for all years and for all scenarios, leading to 5% being diverted to other uses. This leads to projections of total area as shown in Table 10.4 and in Figure 10.3. In the optimistic scenario total area would go up to about 0.90 million ha by the year 2010, while it the conservative scenario it will not reach beyond 0.68 million ha. Since replanting up to 2010 is almost fully determined by trees already in the ground now, new planting and resulting total area scenarios have little influence on replanting projections. Applying the same yield profile and technical progress as experienced in the early nineties leads to levels of normal production as in Table 10.5 and Figure 10.4. A level of just over 650 thousand tonnes is reached in the year 2000 and for the year 2010 levels of 962 thousand, 877 thousand and 771 thousand tonnes are projected for the three scenarios respectively.

Table 10.5: Natural rubber production data and normal production projections

	Optimistic	Pragmatic	Conservative
1990		331563	
1995	507165	506735	506735
2000	658610	655940	651585
2005	816214	783599	742178
2010	961799	877077	771222

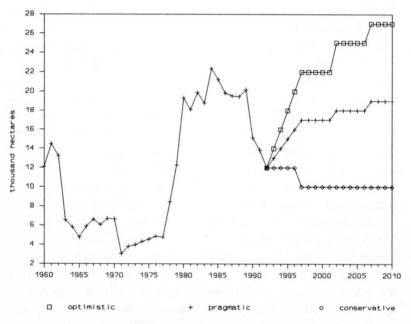

Figure 10.2: New planting of natural rubber, three scenarios

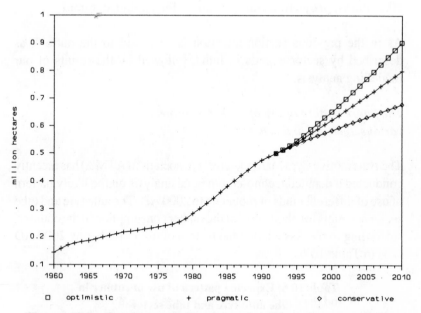

Figure 10.3: Total area under natural rubber, three scenarios

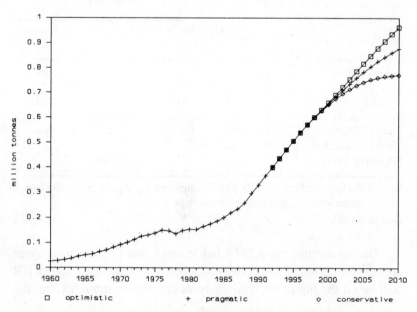

Figure 10.4: Normal production of natural rubber, three scenarios

10.5 Plans, projections and scenarios for rubber demand

As in the previous section attention is first paid to the outlook as
described by sector experts in India, followed by the results of our
modelling analysis.

The future pattern of use of rubber as projected by
various agencies and committees

The Automotive Tyre Manufacturer's Association (ATMA) has recently
conducted a detailed techno-commercial analysis on the likely pattern
of use of different kinds of rubber up to 2000 AD. The auto tyre and tube
sector accounts for about 43% of the rubber consumption in the country.
According to the Association the pattern of use of rubber by 2000 AD
is as in Table 10.6.

Table 10.6: Expected pattern of use of rubber in the auto tyre and tube sector

| | Present | 2000 AD | |
	%	Min %	Max %
Natural Rubber	73.1	65	85
SBR	7.1	5	22
BR	8.5	8	16
Butyl	6.5	6.5 (Avg.)	
Latex (VB/SBR)	1.4	1.1	1.8
Total Synthetic Rubber	23.3		
Reclaimed Rubber	3.4	Not available	

Note: Reclaimed rubber is used in small quantities mainly to produce tyres for animal
        driven vehicles and some small size tyres.
Source: ATMA.

During discussions ATMA has stressed that in India truck tyres
account for the major part of the production and, hence, the usage of NR
will be on the high side. The car tyres can absorb more SR, but the

quantum is restricted mainly due to (i) price of SR bring much higher and (ii) production of car tyres form a lower proportion compared to truck tyres. In the future, the usage pattern may change in favour of SR when its price will come down relative to NR. With the opening up of the Indian economy, the tariff structure is likely to be revised and this may result in stabilizing the Indian price of SR at international levels in the coming years. This has been incorporated in the projections in Table 10.6. In the 1990 publication 'Wheels of India'. Mr. Onkar S. Kanwar, Chairman of ATMA, has also provided data on the preferred mix of NR and SR. In many cases there is a preference for more SR, especially for cross-ply passenger car tyres, rear tractor tyres and 2/3 wheeler tyres.

The All India Rubber Industries Association (AIRIA) has projected the demand pattern as in Table 10.7. The Development Panel of the Government of India, however, projected the demand for 2000 as in Table 10.8.

Table 10.7: Rubber demand projections by type (in 1000 tonnes)

		Present (1991-92)			2000 AD			
		Tyre	Non-Tyre	Total	Tyre	Non-Tyre	Total	%
NR		166	214	380	313	429	742	70
SR	SBR	16	28	44	31	61	92	9
	BR	20	7	27	35	20	55	5
	Butyl	14	8	22	27			
	Others	3	10	13	9	29	65	6
	Total SR 53		53	106	102	110	212	20
RR		7	47	54	15	95	110	10
Total		226	314	540	430	634	1064	100

Table 10.8: Expected pattern of use of rubber

		Minimum	Maximum	Average	%
NR					
	Tyre	230	293	262	(20)
	Non-Tyre	369	419	394	(44)
	Total NR	599	712	656	(72)
SR					
	SBR			110	(12)
	BR			65	(7)
	Others			69	(8)
	Total SR			244	(27)
Total NR & SR				900	(100)

Source: Development Panel of the Government of India:

The above analysis shows that the AIRIA assumes that the present pattern of use will continue up to 2000 AD. However, the Development Panel assumes that the share of SR will increase to 27% from the present level of 22 per cent.

Many raw materials required for the production of SR like styrene, butadiene, extender oil and other chemicals, are imported and subject to substantial duties. At the same time domestic supply of these raw materials is insufficient. However, petrochemical industry is expected to develop gradually and its down stream product would help to meet the feed stock requirements of SR industry. The expansion programmes of the existing units would enable them to realise the economies of scale and reduce their production costs per unit which may narrow the difference between the prices of NR and SR.

Scenarios affecting consumption

To be able to compare the above projections with the results of our model we will present our own projections based on the model as presented in the previous chapters, thereby specifically indicating the additional assumptions used for the standard and the alternative scenarios.

The assumptions

A number of scenarios have been developed and some results are shown graphically. In particular, the impact of different values of the following set of variables is investigated: (1) per capita growth of GDP (2%, 3%, 4%); and (2) prices of vehicles P_{vh} (+0%, +5%, +10%). In both these scenarios the 'pragmatic' planting scenario has been maintained. However, in some instances we confront the outcome of scenarios with either the optimistic as well as the conservative planting scenarios. In the 'prices of vehicles' scenario a per capita GDP growth of three percent.

First of all some assumptions are required regarding the general economic development, in particular the growth of income. In our model income is identical to GDP. Three levels of per capita growth are applied: 2%, 3% and 4%. The development of population has been forecast as well. This variable lies entirely outside the rubber economy and can therefore be assumed to be scenario independent. The suggested forecast for population implies an average annual rate of growth of the population of around 2%, and this growth rate is declining slightly over the years. In 2010 the size of the population is 1,167 millions which compares fairly reasonably with population forecasts by the World Bank.[2] Hence, the implied growth of GDP - the sum of population growth and per capita GDP growth - is around 5%, in case of 3% per capita GDP growth. Some assumption is needed about the general consumer price index. It is assumed that prices rise at an average of 5% per year. This variable is also assumed to be scenario independent. Clearly this will have some impact as price elasticities are all calculated in terms of reactions on relative prices. Both prices of synthetic rubber and natural rubber are determined in the world market: valued in Indian rupees these prices will gradually come closer to each other, and will be the same (and develop accordingly) from 2000 onwards. All other prices in the model - and these concern only prices of vehicles - grow at the same rate as the general consumer price index. Finally the nominal lending rate is assumed to stay fixed. All values of exogenous variables can easily be changed: the choice of the numerical values of exogenous variables is largely arbitrary.

The projections

Deriving the projections of natural rubber consumption for the three GDP per capita scenarios, requires running the full consumption model and deriving projections for each of the GDP per capita scenarios for each type of vehicle and tyre, and the total rubber consumption for tyres as well as for non-tyres rubber consumption. All such projections are available from the authors. Because the emphasis of this report is on rubber, and in particular on natural rubber, we limit projection results to NR- related figures. Running the full model system leads to projections of total rubber consumption (NR + SR) as in Table 10.9.

Table 10.9: Projections of rubber consumption (1000 tonnes) for three income scenarios

	Growth in per capita GDP		
	2%	3%	4%
1995	691	704	717
2000	915	966	1,020
2005	1,169	1,291	1,432
2010	1,452	1,691	1,983

Afterwards these projections are split into natural rubber and synthetic rubber by using the models of the latter part of Chapter 8, using the pragmatic scenario for normal production of natural rubber. The results are shown in Figure 10.5.

Consumption of natural rubber for rubber products consumed in the country will reach around 700,000 tonnes by the turn of the century and by the year 2010 it will have increased to levels ranging from somewhat above 1.0 million for the low scenario to 1.4 million tonnes for the high scenario. A level of around 1.2 million tonnes results for the 3% scenario

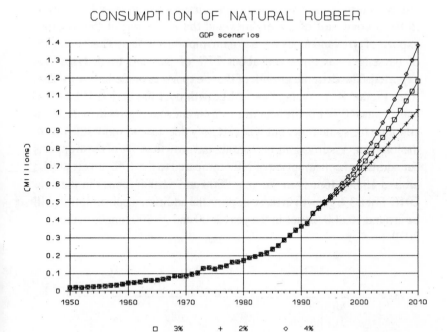

Figure 10.5: Projections of consumption of NR for three GDP per capita scenarios

in 2010. With the assumed production of NR, the so-called 'pragmatic' scenario, the (net) import and (net) export of NR automatically follow Small amounts of export of NR only occur in the low growth scenario (2% per capita GDP) and for a limited period before the turn of the century. Import of NR, however, is substantial especially in the longer run. From Figure 10.6 it is clear that with 3% per capita growth of GDP, imports of NR rise as high as 30,000 tonnes in 2000 and 300,000 tonnes in 2010. Even with the 'optimistic' planting scenario India will be importing from almost nil in 2000 to 200,000 tonnes in 2010.

In the model consumption of rubber is entirely related to the demand for rubber products in the domestic economy. To focus attention on demand for rubber products of domestic origin exclusively has an obvious reason: in the past domestic consumption of rubber products indeed determined consumption of natural rubber entirely.[3] However, in the second half of the eighties and the beginning of the nineties, exports of tyres and tubes seem to gain importance. In 1992 around 10% of passenger car tyres and about 27% of bus and truck tyres was exported. The extreme growth of these exports is immediately evident from Figure 10.7: average annual growth over the period 1980-1990 was around 40%! For the near future these enormous growth rates might continue for some time, but will certainly decrease to modest levels in the long run. Assuming an average annual growth of 5% of these exports the additional consumption of NR (compared to the 1992 level) will be around 18,000 tonnes in the year 2000 and 51,000 tonnes in the year 2010. For a 3% growth in these exports the additional consumption will be around 10,000 tonnes in the year 2000 and 25,000 tonnes in the year 2010.

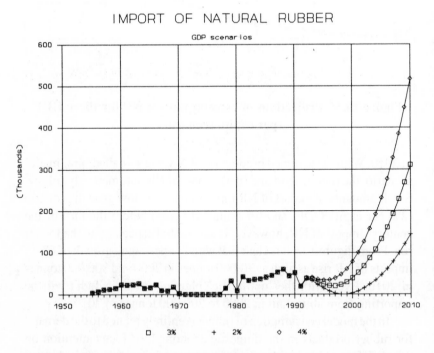

Figure 10.6: **Projections of import of NR for three GDP per capita scenarios**

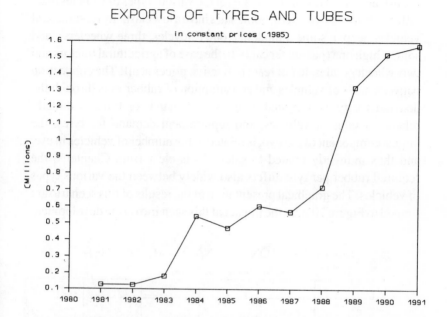

Figure 10.7: Export of tyres and tubes (1980-90)

Scenarios for vehicle prices

To complete the exercises on scenarios on the basis of different domestic developments a scenario has been run with a 10% and 0% annual increase in the nominal price of vehicles. On top of this the nominal lending rate, important in the case of sales of agricultural tractors, grows respectively at the rate of 0.1% and -0.1% annually. As is clear from Chapter 8 it is the real price development that matters in determining the demand for vehicles and not the nominal price development. The assumption with respect to the development of the general consumer price index is maintained. Hence, the first scenario refers to a situation with an annual increase of the relative price of vehicles of 5% and the second one to a situation with an annual decrease of 5%. Note that differential excise duties create price increases as well.

From Chapter 8 it is learnt that sales of the various types of vehicles react differently to relative prices. Some sales have a low elasticity (commercial vehicles, jeeps), some a moderate one (bicycles, three wheelers), and some a high one (passenger cars). In the case of agricultural tractors and two-wheelers sales do not react to relative prices at all! The connection between sales of vehicles and consumption of rubber runs through the demand for tyres. Original equipment demand for tyres is directly related to sales of vehicles, and replacement demand for tyres, the largest component of the two, is related to the number of vehicles in use, and thus indirectly related to sales. As is clear from Chapter 8 the required rubber per tyre differs also widely between the various types of vehicles. The graphical presentation of the results of this scenario are limited to Figure 10.8, as the impact of this scenario on the development

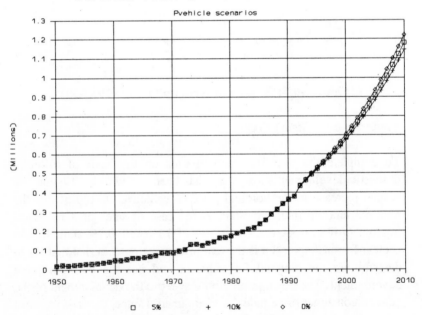

**Figure 10.8: Forecasting consumption of
NR: P_{vh} (0%; + 5%; + 10%)**

of prices, imports and exports is analogous to earlier scenarios. From the figure it becomes clear that the impact of prices of vehicles is moderate. With an increase of prices of vehicles of 10% annually, consumption of natural rubber is 30,000 lower in 2010 compared to the scenario with the standard assumptions. In case of a price increase of vehicles of 0% annually, a consumption of natural rubber of around 30,000 tonnes higher in the year 2010 results.

Development of the share of natural rubber in total

The share of natural rubber in total rubber consumption was 69.9% in 1990. From the calculations it can be shown that this share will very gradually decrease over time. In the year 2000 it will have reached 68.3% and in the year 2010 it is calculated to be 66%. The development of shares is independent of the growth of per capita GDP Of course, it must be added that on a product level a slightly divergent pattern evolves. Figures 10.9 to 10.12 show the developments in a selected number of end-products.

NOTES

1 Indeed, these changes influence the institutional and structural environment of the rubber market, which is required to stay the same for estimated behavioral relationships to have some predictive power. More practically this means that if we want point-estimates for the year 2020 to have some meaning, then at least the institutional and structural environment of the rubber market should remain as it is during the period 1950-1990, the period on which the model is fitted. This can hardly be expected.

2 The World Bank projects a population of 1,007 millions in 2000 (our estimate: 1,003 millions) and 1,350 millions in 2025 (our estimate: 1,371 millions), see World Development Report 1991.

3 This also explains why these exports are not incorporated in the model: the data on which the model is based do not allow such a distinction.

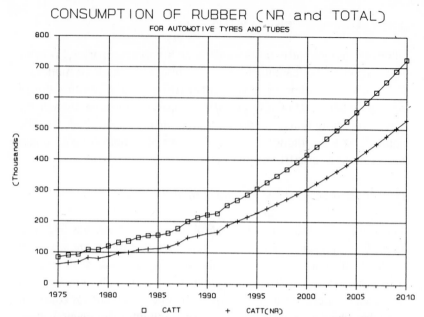

Figure 10.9: Forecasting consumption of NR and total rubber for automotive tyres and tubes (resp. CATT(NR) and CATT)

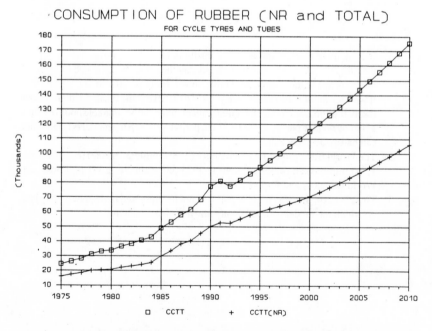

Figure 10.10: Forecasting consumption of NR and total rubber for cycle tyres and tubes (resp. CCTT(NR) and CCTT)

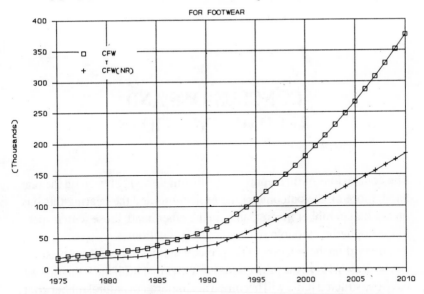

Figure 10.11: Forecasting consumption of NR and total rubber for footwear (resp. CFW(NR) and CFW)

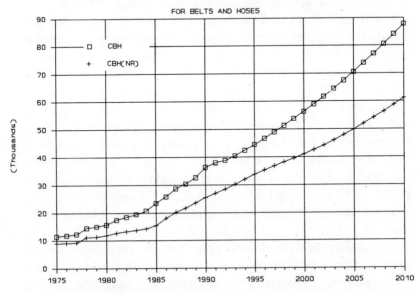

Figure 10.12: Forecasting consumption of NR and total rubber for belts and hoses (resp. CBH(NR) and CBH)

11

CONCLUSIONS AND
RECOMMENDATIONS

The conclusions of this report can be distinguished between on the one hand, those on the outcome of the projections and the bearing this has on the Indian rubber market, and, on the other hand, those with respect to the applied methodology for making projections.

Regarding the outcome of the projections the following conclusions can be drawn. From the projections it follows that in all the scenarios we have constructed India will become a net importer of natural rubber after the turn of the century, even with relatively optimistic production projections. Till the turn of the century production will more or less match consumption. This should be taken very seriously since other research (see Burger and Smit, 1994) indicates that there is likely to be a shortage of NR on a world scale. Obviously, the projections are quite sensitive to exogenous developments, in particular the developments in per capita GDP, the exchange rate, the domestic rate of inflation, the import duty rates on NR and SR, the world market prices of NR and SR and the productivity growth of rubber growers in India. The sensitivity of the outcome justifies the procedure to run simulations: with the uncertainties in the future developments of these exogenous variables, the best approach is to identify and quantify the causal relationships, and, subsequently, calculate and compare the outcomes with different assumptions. Software is available at the Rubber Board in Kottayam and at the Economic and Social Institute in Amsterdam to run many more scenarios and to incorporate recent information and update the full analysis.

Regarding the methodology applied: we can conclude that in the preceding chapters a comprehensive formal description of the Indian rubber economy has been set out. The framework incorporates a great number of causalities that can be observed in the Indian rubber market and is capable of simulating a wide range of developments. Some influences are not incorporated, or incorporated only in an *adhoc* fashion, mostly due to a lack of data: the framework can easily be adjusted to incorporate these influences. This also emphasises the need for adequate and consistent data. Further refinements and extensions are possible in the field of exports of rubber goods, productivity growth in growing NR, the impact of radialisation on tyre distance and tyre weight and the impact of infrastructure on tyre distance. A most attractive result, however, is the possible streamlining of discussions on the future of the Indian rubber market. The framework offers a reasonable way to shift the discussions on the future of the Indian rubber economy, from the purely numerical projections of supply and demand to the exact method used to arrive at these projections.

DERIVATION AND ESTIMATION OF THE DISCARDING FUNCTION

Basic data

New planting of rubber is defined as planting of rubber on a plot, that was covered before with a different crop or with no crop at all. Replanting means that natural rubber was grown there before, that it was "discarded" (e.g. because of age or diseases) and that natural rubber was planted again. If natural rubber was discarded for the above reasons and not replaced we say it was "uprooted".

Using the symbols a^t for total area, n^t for new planting, u^t for uprooting and the subscript t and t-1 for this year and the previous year respectively, then, in mathematical notation:

$$n_t = a_t - a_{t-1} + u_t \qquad (1)$$

where n_t =   new planting of natural rubber in year t
         a_t =   total area under natural rubber at the end of year t
         u_t =   uprooting of natural rubber in year t

Data on u_t normally are not available and can be derived using equation (1) and data on total area and new planting. Suppose that data on replanting are available as well, then two more variables can be calculated:

$$g_t = n_t + r_t \qquad (2)$$

and

$$d_t = r_t + u_t \qquad (3)$$

where g_t = total area planted in a certain year, consisting of new planting (n_t) and replanting (r_t), while total area cleared, or in our terminology, discarded (d_t) consists of area replanted with natural rubber (rt) and area uprooted for other purposes (u_t). So, having three of the six series available, the other three follow by definition.

The general model

A vintage of natural rubber is the natural rubber area planted in a particular year and still available in some other year. For instance, in a hypothetical example, the 1949-vintage could have started at a level of 200, which is new planting + replanting in 1949. At the end of 1949, all trees are still there. However, suppose that for some reason in 1950 1% is removed. So at the end of 1950 the 1949-vintage only has a size of 198. For each of the later years the size of the 1949-vintage can then be derived. The same can be done for the 1950-vintage, the 1951-vintage etc. This means that in any year when natural rubber is produced and when the vintage-composition of natural rubber area is known, information is available on the age of the trees and the year of planting of the trees. Such information on the age of the trees is important since young trees are not productive and older trees become less productive as the years pass by. Knowledge about the year of planting is also important because of technical progress in the quality of the trees. Technical progress implicates that trees planted in 1949 are not as productive after, say, 10 years, that is, in 1959, as trees planted in 1970 would be in 1980. Availability of such information provides an opportunity to obtain more accurate forecasts for the years to come on "normal production": the level of production which would be reached at average levels of tapping, without taking into account the influences of prices.

However, such a vintage composition of rubber area is not available. The starting point obviously is a consistent aggregate database as put in equations (1) to (3). The emphasis in this Appendix is then on a general description of the timing and distribution of discarding. The basic assumption is that the total area which is discarded in some year consists of area with trees of different ages. Intuitively, the older the tree, the more the area that will be discarded in any year. The basic approach is that the probability of a particular area being discarded increases when the area grows older. This is called the discarding function. Figure 1 shows the shape of such a discarding function.

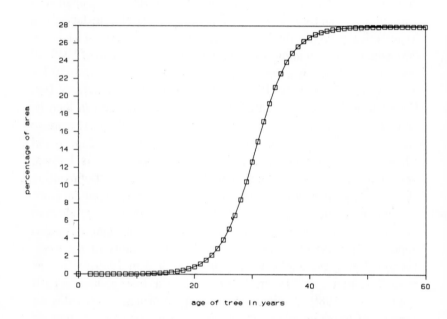

Figure 1: The discarding function

If this S-shaped curve representing the discarding rates is shifted horizontally the average and all probabilities change. A shift to the left would mean that more younger trees would be discarded, while the percentage of very old trees to be discarded would virtually remain unchanged. This appears appropriate for discarding of rubber trees. If discarding is high in a certain year it would be quite unlikely that very high percentages of a given vintage would be discarded in that year. A high level of discarding would rather mean that there is more of a shift in discarding towards younger trees. A similar way of reasoning can be set up in case of low levels of discarding.

The derivation of the share of each age-class in the total area discarded is as follows.

Let

$$p_t = \frac{1}{1 + \alpha_{1t} e^{-\alpha_{2t} t}}$$

which can be written as

$$p_t = \frac{1}{1 + e^{(\mu_t - t)/\gamma}} \tag{4}$$

or as

$$p_t = \frac{1}{1 + e^{(\mu_t - t)/r\mu_t}} \tag{5}$$

where $\mu_t = \ln \alpha_{1t}/\alpha_{2t}$ and $r_t = 1/\ln \alpha_{1t}$. The assumption is that μ_t may change over time. If the original area was a_0, the area left over after t years is

$$a_t = (1 - p_t) a_0 \tag{6}$$

and the area left after t+1 years

$$a_{t+1} = (1 - p_{t+1}) a_0 \tag{7}$$

The relationship between the area in year t and the area in the preceding year t-1 can then be derived as

$$a_t = \frac{1 - p_t}{1 - p_{t-1}} a_{t-1} , \tag{8}$$

so that the fraction of a_{t-1} that is discarded in t is given by

$$q_t = 1 - \frac{1 - p_t}{1 - p_{t-1}} \tag{9}$$

Substituting the expression (5) into this equation leads to

$$q_t = \frac{1 - e^{(-1/r_t\mu_t)}}{1 + e^{(\mu_t - t)/r_t\mu_t}} \tag{10}$$

The maximum, the numerator of equation (10), is shortly referred to as amax and depends on the values of r_t and μ_t:

$$\text{amax}_t = 1 - e^{(-1/r_t\mu_t)} \tag{11}$$

The approach towards determining μ_t

The base year solution

The first step in constructing the empirical models is to find the vintage distribution in the starting year s. The total area a_s is given. If it is assumed that $\mu_t = \mu_s$ for $t \leq s$ then a_s is a distributed lag function of p_t, but now with constant coefficients

So
$$a_s = \sum_\tau a_{s\tau} = \sum_\tau (1 - p_{s-\tau})g_\tau \tag{12}$$

$$a_s = \sum_\tau (1 - \frac{1}{1 + e^{(\mu_s - (s - \tau))/r_t\mu_s}}) g_\tau \tag{13}$$

The right hand side of (13) is regarded as a function $f(\mu_s)$ so $a_s = f(\mu_s)$ by definition. This equation cannot be solved easily, because of the highly non-linear way, in which appears in the equation. The solution is found in an iterative manner. The iteration is based on the Newton procedure for finding such a solution. This procedure is derived from a first order approximation of the optimal ms in each step, while the ms that solves the equation is denoted μ_s.

Basically, r_t should be determined simultaneously with μ_s. However, in order to avoid estimation problems, it is assumed at this stage, since $v_s = r_s \mu_s$ (by definition) and $\sigma_s = v_s \pi / \sqrt{3}$ (for the logistic curve), so $\sigma_s = r_s \pi / \sqrt{3} \ \mu_s$; assuming now a reasonable ratio between σ_s and μ_s e.g. $\sigma_s = .18 \ \mu_s$ then $r_s = 0.1$. During estimation sensitivity test can be applied regarding the assumptions on the level of r. In the following we will skip the time subscript to r.

The consecutive years

From year s + 1 onwards, the following approach is followed:

$$d_t \quad = \quad \sum_{\tau} d_{t\tau} \tag{14}$$

where $d_{t\tau}$ = discarding on vintage τ in year t and

$$d_{t\tau} \quad = \quad q_{t\tau} a_{t-1,\tau} \tag{15}$$

with $q_{t\tau}$ given in (10). For each consecutive year t and for the assumed value of r = 0.1, μ_t is fixed because

$$d_t = \sum_{\tau} \frac{1 - e^{(-1/r\mu_t)}}{1 + e^{(\mu_t - (t-\tau))/r\mu_t}} * a_{t-1,\tau} \text{ for } \tau < t \tag{16}$$

The method of determining μ_t for each t runs parallel to the solution procedure for the base year s. For each consecutive year, μ_t is determined in this way, followed by $d_{t,\tau}$ and $a_{t,\tau}$, because for t = 1, $a_{t-1,\tau}$ is known from the base year solution, after which the iterative method is applied again, using

$$a_{t,\tau} \quad = \quad a_{t-1,\tau} - d_{t\tau} = (1 - q_{t\tau}) \ a_{t-1,\tau} \text{ for } \tau < t \tag{17}$$

and

$$a_{t,t} \quad = \quad g_t \tag{18}$$

DERIVATION OF THE AGE DISTRIBUTION OF NATURAL RUBBER AREA IN 1955-56

Table 1, below, provides the data available. The derivation starts from the 200 ha. in 1902. Next data is an area of 11,900 ha. in 1910. Hence, new plantings must have been at least 11,700 in the intermediate 8 years. Some discarding may, however, have taken place in the meantime due to storms, diseases, etc. This discarding is given by the discarding function, for which a mu (μ) equal to 30.5 was assumed. This implies that - ideally - the average age of discarded trees is 30.5 years, and that at most some 28 per cent of an age group is discarded in one year. For the period until 1910 this works out in a discarded area of only 2.7 ha., which must be added to the new plantings in order to arrive at the given total area in 1910. The next check point is 1925 for which the net area reported is 30,886 ha. Total paintings are given as 1950 ha. Normal discarding at mu=30.5 would lead to discarding during 1925 of 88 ha., so that 1950-88=1862 is new planting and the balance is taken to be replanted. Uprooting is assumed to be nil in these years. To come from 11,900 in 1910 to 30,886-1862=29,024 in 1925, taking "normal" discarding into account, the average new and replanting must have been 1230.541. This we have assumed for all years 1911-1924.

Area figures for 1925 to 1954 are available, though they are not accurate to the extent desired. McFadyean (1944) estimates the age distribution of rubber growing area in India at the end of 1940 as 11,455 acres (4636 ha.) 0-5 years old, 2445 acres (989 ha.) 6-10 years old, 45,004 acres (18212 ha.) 10 to 15 years old and 77723 acres (31453 ha.) more than 15 years old. Based on these data and other available information (indicated in the note to Table 1) the annual estimated area is presented in Table 1. The area, which was around 48,000 ha. in 1930 should have gone down to around 45,000 ha. around 1938 and thereafter improved to 47,200 ha. in 1940 and 81,217 in 1954/55.

Table 1: Area planted and total area 1902-1954

Year	New planting	Discards	Re-planting	Total area	'mu' (μ)
1955/56	9342	5211	719	86067	31.15
1954	4291	1411	455	81217[b]	40.94
1953	1746	735	315	77882	44.89
1952	955	366	366	76556	48.70
1951	686	270	270	75601	49.78
1950	886	446	446	74915	45.67
1949	1025	127	127	74029	53.00
1948	1668	268	268	73004	46.92
1947	2557	205	205	71336	47.60
1946	2344	170	170	68779	47.72
1945	4754	65	65	66435	53.22
1944	4942	378	378	61681	40.92
1943	6174	124	124	56739	46.43
1942	2464	882	882	50565	34.79
1941	901	508	508	48101	37.07
1940	807	884	884	47200[c]	33.68
1939	1340	305	305	46370	38.29
1938	205	584	584	45017	34.31
1937	0	551	530	45329	33.89
1936	0	1017	257	45817	30.50
1935	0	918	40	46478	30.50
1934	0	807	486	47245	30.50
1933	0	691	69	46828	30.50
1932	0	575	88	47450	30.50
1931	0	466	403	47937	30.50
1930	179	164	164	48000[a]	33.88

(contd.)

1929	441	280	280	47821	30.50
1928	2145	213	213	47380	30.50
1927	4986	160	160	45235	30.50
1926	9364	119	119	40250	30.50
1925	1862	88	88	30886[a]	30.50

1911-1925 rp+np = 1240
1903-1910 rp+np = 1463
area '10=   11900[a]
area '02=   200[a]
a = 'A short note on Rubber Plantation Industry in India' (1974)
b = Indian Rubber Statistics (1991) Rubber Board (RB)
c = 'Plantation Enquiry Commission Report' (1956) for figures up to 1950 and for
      remaining period IRS

Figure 2 shows the resulting graphs of total area from 1902
onwards. As can be seen, our data suggest a slight fall in total area after
1927, contrary to data published in IRS18.

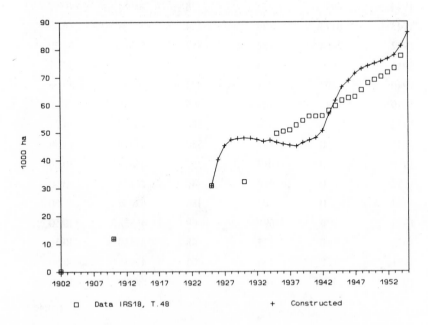

Figure 2: Total area, IRS data and model-constructed estimates

The assumptions and data on total planted area in all years are given in Figure 3. The steep increase in 1926 clearly stands out and, as we shall see later, its effects will be felt until well into the 1960s.

After 1947, the increase in total area may have been slightly higher than that given in IRS, unless discarding has been very low. Assuming normal discarding, we estimate that substantial area must have been planted in all of the years 1947-1954 in order to arrive at the total area and the plantings of 1954-55. After the earlier years of much plantings, we assumed them to come gradually down in 1950 and rise again in 1951 in view of the high rubber prices at that time.

This establishes the age distribution of 1955. Total plantings in 1954 have been 4746 ha., and in 1955 no less than 10061 is planted. The age distribution over the other age groups is given in Figure 4. It can be seen that of the 9483 ha. planted in 1926, 8392 ha. still remains in 1955.

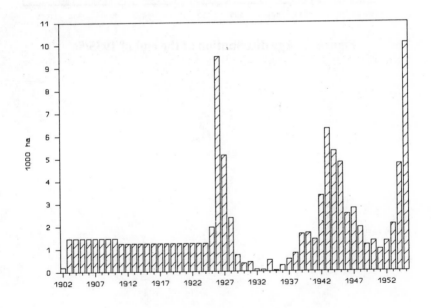

Figure 3: Total plantings 1902-1955

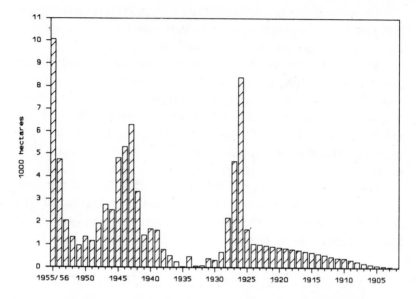

Figure 4: Age distribution at the end of 1955/56

APPENDIX C

TECHNICAL CHANGE AND YIELD PROFILES

Similar to the approaches followed for Malaysian smallholdings, Indonesia and Thailand (see Burger and Smit, 1989), we start from a standard yield profile in terms of production per ha. in which constant tapping intensity, good tapping practice, and normal decline of density is assumed. The shape is given Figure 6.6 of the main text.

The extent to which these new varieties contribute to production depends on the yield profiles. Data on yields per variety are difficult to

Table 1: Yields of NR varieties (estates)

Year of tapping	pb86	rrim600	gtl	pb28/59	rrii105	tjirl[a]	tjirl[b]
1	520	681	672	715	832	462	492
2	749	1164	924	1138	1346	618	683
3	913	1137	1079	1359	1554	777	795
4	1057	1277	1173	1493	1622	917	834
5	1180	1387	1246	1432	1896	937	845
7	1294	1588	1780	1501	1673	1110	888
8	1347	1563	1665	2060	2057	1294	916
9	1334	1532	1739	1756	1365[c]		986
10	1285	1508	1756	1624	1687[c]	942	
11	1223	1332	1704	1586			
12	1227	1389	1551	1396			
13	1147	1855	1659	999			
14	1178	1527	1330				
15	1221						

Source: Toms Joseph and Haridasan (no date);
a   refers to replanting on smallholdings, source: Haridasan (no date);
b   clonal seedlings, source: Krishnan Kutty & Sreenivasan (1985);
c   single observations only.

collect, as smallholders often grow a mixture of varieties and hardly keep record of production. Table 1 shows therefore mainly data from estates. To judge the performance of the varieties, we compared the figures with the standard yield profile and checked whether we can assume that the profile was similar, i.e. only differed in proportion, but not in shape. An analysis was made of the relative yield levels, i.e. the yields divided by the standard yield. Table 2 summarize the outcomes regarding average ratio, and estimated trend parameter in a regression analysis of yield ratios against year of tapping.

One group of data are taken from Toms Joseph and Haridasan (undated), the second group from Krishnan Kutty, year et al (1982, 1985). The first group of observations are based on up to 15 years of tapping, and therefore are more relevant for our purpose. The data showed that in particular the second year of tapping was too low in the standard yield profile.

Table 2: Relative yield ratios of various clones

type of clone	no of observ.	ratio	avg %	est. trend parm	signif- icant?	
PB86	15		61	-.007	yes	data: Toms Joseph
RRIM600	14	77		-.012	yes	and Haridasan
GT1	14	76		-.002.	no	
PB28/59	13	80		-.027	yes	
RRII-105	10	95		-.039	yes	
TJIR1(smh)	8		55	.004	yes	
PB86	10	68		.003	no	data: Krishnan Kutty
PRIM605	10	78		-.049	yes·	et al.
GG1	10	69		-.013	yes	
GG2	10	65		-.008	no	
TJIR1 bg	10	55		-.004	no	
TJIR1 cs	10	50		-.019	yes	

Major types like TJIR1, RRIM600 and RRII-105 reach levels of the average ratio of 55%, 77% and 95%. Estimated trend parameters are mostly negative, showing that relative yields of the clones are higher in the earlier years of tapping. This is particularly the case in the first four years of tapping and relative yields are rather constant afterwards. Similar regression estimates of the trend parameters after 5 years of tapping gave only significant parameters for PB86 in the first group (6-15 years of tapping) and for RRIM605 in the second group (6-10 years of tapping).

We draw the conclusion that as yet no strong evidence exists for changing the yield profile, with the exception of the early years of tapping. This is incorporated in the model by allowing for a one-year shorter immaturity period for the RRII-105 clone.

QUESTIONNAIRE FOR THE SURVEY

THE RUBBER BOARD
IDPAD study on Natural Rubber

Questionnaire for collection of information

I   Name and address of the rubber holder

II   Family position as on 31-03-1992
Relation to the head   Age   Education   Occupation
Head of the family
Other members   1
    2
    3
    4
    5
    6

III   If the entire area operated is not contiguous, answer the
following (as on 31-03-1992)
No of Parcel   Distance from the house Area (ha.)   Crop cultivated
1
2
3

IV   How you became a rubber cultivator?
Rubber area inherited/Rubber area purchased
Planted rubber in fresh land/Planted rubber removing other crops

V   Source of income of the family during 1991-92: Rs.
(a) Rubber
(b) Other crops
(c) Employment
(d) Others (specify)

VI Details of rubber area during 1001-92

Year of planting	Area (ha.)	No. of trees	Planting material	Which year tapping started	Tapping system	Produc- tion	No. of trees tapped	No. of tap- ping days obtained	Whether tapping rest given during		Whether rainguarded Yes/No
									Feb.-Mar. 1992 Yes/No	June-Aug. 1992 Yes/No	
(1)	(2)	(3)	(4)	(5)	(6)	(7)	(8)	(9)	(10)	(11)	(12)

Family Labour		Hired Labour				Financial assistance received			
Tapping (MD)	Other works (MD)	Tapping (MD)	Other works (MD)	Wage rate (R./day)	Current price (Rs./kg)	Year	Amount (Rs.)	Purpose	Source
(13)	(14)	(15)	(16)	(17)	(18)	(19)	(20)	(21)	(22)

MD: Man days

VII Plan for replanting existing rubber area

Year of planting of existing rubber which is proposed to be uprooted	Area (ha.)	When you want to uproot (year) area	Crop to be planted in the uprooted	If answer to (4) is rubber			Whether the area suitable for planting other crops? If so, planting crops	If answer to (4) is not rubber, reason for
				Why you want to plant rubber period	How will you finance the immaturity which?			
(1)	(2)	(3)	(4)	(5)	(6)		(7)	(8)

If answer to (9) is rubber

What was grown before existing rubber trees	Age at which it was uprooted	No. of trees at the time of up-rooting	Yield per ha. at the time of uprooting (kg)	How the immaturity period is financed	If answer to (9) is not rubber	
					Which crop was cultivated in the area	Why it was removed and planted with rubber
(9)	(10)	(11)	(12)	(13)	(14)	(15)

VIII Plan for planting/replanting existing area planted with crops other than rubber/vacant land

Name of crop other than rubber	Area (ha.)	Year of planting	Financial assistance, if any received			Production 1991-92	Current price	Family labour during 1991-92 (MD)	Hired labour	
			Year	Nature of assistance	Source				During 1991-92 (MD)	Wage rate per day (Rs.)
(1)	(2)	(3)	(4)	(5)	(6)	(7)	(8)	(9)	(10)	(11)

If answer to (12) is rubber

What was grown before in the area	Age at which tree uprooted	No. of rubber trees in the area	Average yield (kg/ha)	Amount received for the tree	How immature area financed	If answer to (12) is other crops why you have not planted rubber	When do you want to remove the existing crop	Crop to be planted in the area	If answer to (20) is rubber	
									Why you want to plant rubber	How will you finance the immaturity period
(12)	(13)	(14)	(15)	(16)	(17)	(18)	(19)	(20)	(21)	(22)

IX a) If you have immature area, indicate the type of intercrops/trees in the rubber area during 1991-92.

Name of trees/crops

Income from intercrops/trees (Rs.)

b) If you have other trees/crops in the yielding rubber area during 1991-92:

Name of trees/crops

Income (Rs.)

c) Other source of income from rubber area during 1991-92:

Cattle rearing (Rs.)

Poultry (Rs.)

Bee/hive (Rs.)

Others (Rs.)

Total (Rs.)

X Remarks of the enumerator

Date of visit: Name of signature of the
Place: enumerator:

REFERENCES

All India Rubber Industries Association, Bombay (various issues).

Ashokanand (1988), Modern Trends in Retreading, *Rubber Asia,* Vol 2 (10).

Association of Indian Automobile Manufacturers (1985), *Statistical profile,* 1990 & 1991, Bombay.

Automotive Component Manufacturers Association of India (1990-91 and 1991-92), Automotive Industry of India - Facts and Figures.

Automotive Tyre Manufacturers Association (undated), Tyre Retreading, internal ATMA report.

Automotive Tyre Manufacturers Association (1991), Elastomer Demand Projections in Respect of Tyre Industry.

Automotive Tyre Manufacturers Association (1992), Tyre and Vehicle Production Statistics, Delhi.

Automotive Tyre Manufacturers Association (1993), Domestic Demand and Export Promotions 1992-93 to 2000-2001, Delhi.

Burger, K. & Smit, H.P. (1989), Long-Term and Short-Term Analysis of the Natural Rubber Market, *Weltwirtschaftliches Archiv,* 125(4).

Burger, K. & Smit, H.P. (1994), Natural Rubber in the coming Decades: Shortages ahead? Proceedings of the International Rubber Study Group, Colombo, Sri Lanka, 23-28 May.

Government of India, Ministry of Finance, Central Excise Tariff, various issues.

Government of India, Ministry of Finance, Customs Tariff, various issues.

Government of India, Ministry of Finance, Economic Survey, 1988-89 to 1991-92, Delhi.

Government of India, Ministry of Petroleum, Indian Oil Corporation, various issues, New Delhi.

Government of India, Directorate General of Commercial Intelligence and Statistics, Monthly Statistics of Foreign Trade of India, Vol. 1, Exports, Vol. 2 and Imports, various issues.

Government of India, Transport Research Division, Ministry of Surface Transport, Motor Transport Statistics of India, various issues.

Government of India (1988), Motor Vehicles Act, Delhi.

Government of India, Central Statistical Organisation, Ministry of Planning, *Statistical Abstract*, various issues.

Government of India, Ministry of Industrial Development (1985), Report on the Committee on Auto Tyres and Tubes.

Government of India, Ministry of Commerce, *Import and Export Policy*, various issues.

Government of India, Planning Commission, various issues of Five Year Plans.

Government of India, Plantation Enquiry Commission Report (1956).

Government of Kerala (1988), Department of Economics and Statistics, Statistics for Planning, Trivandrum.

Guha, P.K. & Gadjah Tunngal, P.T. (1990), Retreading of Radial Ply Tyres, *Rubber News*.

Haridasan, V. (1978), Rubber plantation industry in India; first world war to independence, *Rubber Board Bulletin*, 15(3&4).

Haridasan, V. (undated), Replanting of small holdings - the Indian experience, Rubber Board, Kottayam.

Jain, R.K. (1991), Future of rubber goods industry, paper presented at the National Rubber Conference organised by the Indian Rubber Growers Association on 3-10-1991 at Cochin, *Rubber India*.

Jorgenson, F. & Wentzel-Larsen, T. (1990), Car Holding, Scrappage and Purchase, *Journal of Transport Economics and Policy*.

Juster, F.T. & Wachtel, P. (1972), Anticipatory and Objective Models of Models Durable Goods Demand, *American Economic Review*, Vol. 62.

Krishnan Kutty, P.N., Jacob, George & Haridasan, V. (1982), Evaluation of planting material under commercial planting - first report, *Rubber Board Bulletin*, 17(4).

Krishnan Kutty, P.N. & Sreenivasan, K.G. (1985) Evaluation of planting material under commercial planting - second report, *Rubber Board*

Bulletin, Vol. 20(2).

Kuriakose, Baby (1992), Tyre Retreading: New Trends, *Indian Rubber and Plastics Age.*

Kurian, J. (1991), Retreading Industry - Need for Standardisation of Inputs, *Rubber India.*

Makundan Menon, P. & Unny, R.G. (1990), Natural rubber production prospects in India to meet the entire growing requirements of general purpose elastomers on a long term basis, Rubber Board, Kottayam.

McFadyean, Sir Andrew (1944), *The History of Rubber Regulation 1934-1943,* London: Allen & Unwin.

Ministry of Industry, GOI, Report on the Committee on Tyres and Tubes (1985) and Sub-Group on NR Panel.

Modi, V.K. (1988), The auto tyre-industry - prospects and problems, text of speech delivered at the first Meeting of the Development Council for Tyres and Tubes Industry held at 1908-1988 at New Delhi, *Rubber News.*

M/s. Synthetics and Chemicals Ltd. (1990), Correspondence and Annual reports

Narayana, D. (1989), The Motor Vehicle Industry in India, Centre for Development Studies, Occasional Papers Series.

National Council of Applied Economics Research, Ten-Year Perspective Plan for Rubber (1980-81 to 1989-90), New Delhi.

National Council of Applied Economics Research, Demand for Agricultural Tractors, New Delhi.

Profile of MRF: India's Leading Tyre Company, *Rubber Trends,* September, 1991.

Ramakrishna Pillai, K. (1974), Response of small growers of rubber to the aid schemes of the Rubber Board - Report of a Sample Survey, Rubber Board, Kottayam.

Reserve Bank of India Bulletin, various issues.

Rubber Board of India, Sixth, Seventh and Eighth Five-Year Plan for Natural Rubber.

Rubber Board of India, 1947 - A short note on rubber plantation industry in India.

Rubber Board of India, *Indian Rubber Statistics,* several issues.

Sekhar, Tan Sri B.C. (1988), *Natural Rubber Supply in India. Scenario upto 2000 AD,* AIRIA, Bombay.

Smit, H.P. (1982), *The World Rubber Economy to the Year 2000,* unpublished Ph.D. Thesis, Free University, Amsterdam.

Smit, Hidde P. (1984), *Forecasts for the world rubber economy to the year 2000,* Globe Industry, report, No.2, London, Macmillan.

Sumner, A.J.M., Review of the Status of Automation in Tyre Manufacture, *Indian Rubber and Plastic Age,* Annual 1991.

Tharian George K., Haridasan, V. & Sreekumar, B. (1988), Role of Government and Structural Changes in Rubber Plantation Industry, *Economic and Political Weekly,* November 26.

The Indian Tyre Industry and its Markets, *Rubber Trends,* September, 1989.

The Non-Tyre Rubber Industry in India, *Rubber Trends,* March, 1990.

Toms, Joseph & Haridasan, V. (undated), Evaluation of planting material under commercial planting - third report, Rubber Board, Kottayam.

Toms, Joseph, Punnoose, K.I., Haridasan, V., Mathew, M. & Mani, Jacob (1989), A Survey of agro-economic conditions of the small rubber growers in Anakkara village of Idukki District, *Rubber Board Bulletin,* 24(1).

UNIDO (1990), India, New Dimensions of Industrial Growth, *Industrial Developments Review Series.*

UNIDO (1990), India, New Dimensions of Industrial Growth, *Industrial Development Review Series.*

Unny, R.G. & Jacob, George (1972), *Rubber Small Holdings in India,* Rubber Board, Kottayam.

Unny, R.G. & Haridasan, V. (1974), A Study of co-operative Rubber Marketing Sector, Rubber Board, Kottayam.

INDEX